Popular
ANTIQUES
and their Values
1875-1950

Tony Curtis

The publishers wish to express their sincere thanks to the following for their involvement and assistance in the production of this volume:

Edited By TONY CURTIS
Text By EELIN McIVOR

ANNETTE CURTIS
TRACEY BLACK
LOUISE SCOTT-JONES
NICKY FAIRBURN
CATRIONA McKINVEN
DONNA BONAR
JACQUELINE LEDDY
FRANK BURRELL
JAMES BROWN
EILEEN BURRELL

A CIP catalogue record for this book is available from the British Library.

ISBN 0 - 86248 - 121 - X

Copyright © Lyle Publications MCMXC
Glenmayne, Galashiels, Scotland.

Introduction

Beyond its purely aesthetic appeal, an article of a bygone age frequently has one great advantage over that which is produced at the present time: it generally appreciates in value as each year passes and few people in this day and age would disagree with the proposition that a beautiful piece whose investment potential may be as high as that of property is an asset indeed.

The purpose of this publication is to make it easy for those either buying, selling, or merely interested in the value of the pieces in their own home, to identify and have a knowledge of the price an Antique Dealer is likely to pay for a piece in average condition.

The items chosen are, on the whole, representative of the middle section of the market with the addition of a few rare pieces, which, although not to be found in every corner shop, command such surprisingly high prices as to make their inclusion of benefit to the reader.

The current value of an antique varies enormously in different areas. What is fashionable in one county may be totally disregarded in another, which accounts for the amount of trading between dealers who come from different parts of the country. This will also happen when one dealer is more knowledgeable than another or a specialist in a particular field. One dealer may find it more profitable to turn his stock over frequently in order to keep his money 'working' for him and will therefore buy and sell while showing a very modest profit. Another may treat his stock as an investment and can afford to wait for a higher price.

When making any calculations it is wise to remember that the dealer may have to spend as much having the piece put in a saleable condition as he has originally paid for that same item. One must also allow for his profit margin. At all times the cost of restoration must be taken into account, for even the most rare piece, if damaged is imperfect, and therefore of lesser value than the perfect example.

This book will, however, give a fair idea of the current value which I hope will be of assistance to those who, while having an appreciation of the look and feel of antiques, may lack the confidence to plunge in at the deep end.

Printed and bound in Great Britain by
Butler & Tanner Ltd, Frome and London

Acknowledgements

Abbotts Auction Rooms, The Auction Rooms, Campsea Ashe, Woodbridge, Suffolk.
Anderson & Garland, Anderson House, Market Street, Newcastle-upon-Tyne NE1 6XA.
Bagshaws, 17 High Street, Uttoxeter.
Banks & Silvers, Fine Art Dept., 66 Foregate Street, Worcester.
Bearnes, Rainbow, Avenue Road, Torquay, Devon TQ2 5TG.
Biddle & Webb, Ladywood Middleway, Birmingham, B16 0PP.
Blackhorse Agencies, 18 Guy Street, Leamington Spa.
Boardman, Fine Art Auctioneers, Station Road Corner, Haverhill, Suffolk CB9 0EY.
Bonhams, Montpelier Galleries, Montpelier Street, Knightsbridge, London SW7 1HH.
Bonhams of Chelsea, 65-69 Lots Road, London SW10 0RN.
Michael J. Bowman, 6 Haccombe House, near Netherton, Newton Abbott, Devon TQ12 4SJ.
Bracketts, 27-29 High Street, Tunbridge Wells, Kent TN1 1UU.
British Antique Exporters, Burgess Hill, West Sussex RH15 9RX.
R. Brocklesbury, 8 Whites Road, Bitterne, Southampton SO2 7NQ.
Brogden & Co., 38 & 39 Silver Street, Loncoln LN2 1EM.
Graham Brierley/Brian Bates, 10 Madeley Street, Tunstall.
Wm. H. Brown, Westgate Hall, Grantham, Lincolnshire NG31 6LT.
Lawrence Butler Fine Arts Salerooms, Marine Walk, Hythe, Kent CT21 5AJ.
Cantabrian Antiques, 16 Park Street, Linton, North Devon.
Capes Dunn & Co., The Auction Galleries, 38 Charles Street, Manchester M1 7DB.
Chancellors Hollingsworth, 31 High Street, Ascot, Berkshire SL5 7HG.
H. C. Chapman & Son, The Auction Mart, North Street, Scarborough YO11 1DL.
Christie's, Cornelis Schuytstraat 57, 1071 JG, Amsterdam, Netherlands.
Christie's (International) S.A., 8 Place de la Taconnerie, 1204 Geneva, Switzerland.
Christie's (Hong Kong) Ltd., 3607 Edinburgh Tower, 15 Queens Road, Hong Kong.
Christie's, 8 King Street, St James's, London SW1Y 6QT.
Christie's (Monaco) S.A.M., Park Palace, 98000 Monte Carlo, Monaco.
Christie's, 502 Park Avenue, new York, NY 10022, USA.
Christie's, 219 East 67th Street, New York, NY 10021, USA.
Christie's Scotland, 164-166 Bath Street, Glasgow G2 4TG.
Christie's South Kensington Ltd., 85 Old Brompton Road, London SW7 3LD.
Chrystals Auctions, The Mart, Bowring Road, Ramsay, Isle of Man.
A. J. Cobern, The Grosvenor Salerooms, 93b Eastbank Street, Southport PR8 1DG.
Coles, Knapp & Kennedy, Georgian Rooms, Ross-on-Wye, Herefordshire HR9 5HL.
Bruce D.. Collins, Fine Arts Gallery, Box 113, Denmark, Maine, USA.
Cooper Hirst, Goldlay House, Parkway, Chelmsford, Essex CM2 7PR.
Cooper & Tanner, 44a Commercial Road, Shepton Mallet, Somerset.
County Group, 102 High Street, Tenterden, Kent TN30 6AU.
The Crested China Co., The Station House, Driffield, East Yorkshire YO25 7PY.
Dacre, Son & Hartley, 1-5 The Grove, Ilkley, West Yorkshire LS29 8HS.
Dee & Atkinson, The Exchange Saleroom, Driffield, North Humberside, YO25 7LJ.
Dowell Lloyd & Co. Ltd., 118 Putney Bridge Road, Putney, London SW15 2NQ.
Dreweatt Neate, Donnington Priory, Donnington, Newbury, Berkshire RG13 2JE.
Du Mouchelles Art Galleries Co., 409 E. Jefferson Avenue, Detroit, Michigan 48226, USA.
Hy Duke & Son, Fine Art Salerooms, Weymouth Avenue, Dorchester DT1 1DG.
Robt. C. Eldred Co. Inc., Route 6a (PO Box 796), East Dennis, MA 02641, USA.
Peter Eley, Western House, 98-100 High Street, Sidmouth, Devon EX10 8EF.
R. H. Ellis & Sons, 44/46 High Street, Worthing, West Sussex NB11 1LL.
Graham H. Evans, Auction Sales Centre, The Market Place, Kilgetty, Dyfed SA68 0UG.
Fellows & Sons, Bedford House, 88 Hagley Road, Edgbaston, Birmingham.
John D. Fleming & Co., 8 Fore Street, Dulverton, Somerset.
John Francis, S.O.F.A.A., Chartered Surveyors, Curiosity Sale Rooms, King Street, Carmarthen.
Galerie Moderne, 3 Rue du Parnasse, Bruxelles, Belgium.
Geering & Colyer, 22/26 High Street, Tunbridge Wells, Kent TN1 1XA.
Geering & Colyer (Black Horse Agencies), Highgate, Hawkhurst, Kent TD18 4AD.
Glendinning's, Blenstock House, 7 Blenheim Street, New Bond Street, London W1Y 9LD.
Goss & Crested China Co., 62 Murray Road, Horndean, Hampshire PO8 9JL.
Graves, Son & Pilcher, 71 Church Road, Hove, East Sussex BN3 2GL.
W. R. J. Greenslade & Co., 13 Hammet Street, Taunton, Somerset TA1 1RN.

ACKNOWLEDGEMENTS

Habsburg Feldman SA, 202 rue du Grand-Lancy, 1213 Onex-Geneve, Switzerland.

Halifax Property Service, 53 High Street, Tenterden, Kent.

Halifax Property Services — St John Vaughan with John Hogbin, 53 High Street, Tenterden, Kent.

Hamptons Fine Art, 93 High Street, Godalming, Surrey.

Giles Haywood, The Auction House, St John's Road, Stourbridge, West Midlands DY8 1EW.

Heatheringtons Nationwide, The Amersham Auction Rooms, 125 Station Road, Amersham, Bucks.

Andrew Hilditch & Son Ltd., 19 The Square, Sandbach, Cheshire CW11 0AT.

Hobbs & Chambers, 'At the Sign of the Bell', Market Place, Cirencester, Gloucestershire.

Hobbs Parker, Romney House, Ashford Market, Ashford, Kent TN23 1PG.

Jacobs & Hunt, Lavant Street, Petersfield, Hampshire GU32 3EF.

G. A. Key, Aylsham Salerooms, Palmers Lane, Aylsham, Norfolk NR11 6EH.

King & Chasemore, (Nationwide Anglia) West Street, Midhurst, West Sussex GU29 9NG.

Lalonde Fine Art (Prudential Bristol), 71 Oakfield Road, Clifton, Bristol, Avon BS8 2BE.

Lambert & Foster (County Group), The Auction Sale Rooms, 102 High Street, Tenterden.

W. H. Lane & Son, Fine Art Auctioneer & Valuers, 64 Morrab Road, Penzance, Cornwall.

Langlois Ltd., Westaway Rooms, Don Street, St Helier, Jersey, Channel Islands.

Lawrence Fine Art, South Street, Crewkerne, Somerset TA18 8AB.

Lawrence's, Fine Art Auctioneers, Norfolk House, 80 High Street, Bletchingley, Surrey.

David Lay, The Penzance Auction House, Alverton, Penzance, Cornwall TR18 4RE.

Locke & England, Walton House, 11 The Parade, Leamington Spa.

Lots Road Chelsea Auction Galleries, 71 Lots Road, Chelsea, London SW10 0RN.

Michael G. Matthews, The Devon Fine Art Auction House, Dowel Street, Honiton, Devon.

McKenna's Auctioneers & Valuers, Bank Salerooms, Harris Court, Clitheroe, Lancashire.

Miller & Company, Lemon Quay Auction Rooms, Truro, Cornwall TR1 2LW.

Moore, Allen & Innocent, 33 Castle Street, Cirencester, Gloucestershire GL7 1QD.

Morphets, 4-6 Albert Street, Harrogate, North Yorkshire HG1 1JL.

D. M. Nesbit & Co., 7 Clarendon Road, Southsea, Hampshire PO5 2ED.

Michael Newman, The Central Auction Rooms, St Andrews Cross, Plymouth PL1 3DG.

James Norwich Auctions Ltd., Head Office, 33 Timberhill, Norwich, Norfolk NR1 3LA.

Onslow's, Metrostore, Sands Wharf, Townmead Road, London SW6 2RZ.

Osmond Tricks, Regent Street Auction Rooms, Clifton, Bristol, Avon BS8 4HG.

Outhwaite & Litherland, "Kingsway Galleries", Fontenoy Street, Liverpool, Merseyside L3 2BE.

J. R. Parkinson Son & Hamer Auctions, The Auction Room, Rochdale Road, Bury, Lancashire.

Phillips, 65 George Street, Edinburgh EH2 2JL.

Phillips, 207 Bath Street, Glasgow G2 4DH.

Phillips, Blenstock House, 7 Blenheim Street, New Bond Street, London W1Y 0AS.

Phillips New York, 406 East 79th Street, New York, NY 10021, USA.

Phillips West Two, 10 Salem Road, London W2 4BU.

Prudential Fine Art Auctioneers, Trinity House, 114 Northenden Road, Sale, Manchester.

Prudential Fine Art Auctioneers, 71 Oakfield Road, Bristol.

Prudential Fine Art Auctioneers, 13 Lime Tree Walk, Sevenoaks, Kent.

Reeds Rains Prudential, Trinity House, 114 Northenden Road, Manchester M33 3HD.

Rennie's, 1 Agincourt Street, Monmouth.

Riddetts of Bournemouth, Richmond Hill, Bournemouth.

Rosebery's Fine Art Ltd., 3 & 4 Hardwicke Street, London EC1R 4RB.

Russell, Baldwin & Bright, The Fine Art Saleroom, Ryelands Road, Leominster HR6 8JG.

Sandoe Luce Panes, Wotton Auction Rooms, Wotton-under-Edge, Gloucestershire GL12 7EB.

Robt. W. Skinner Inc., Bolton Gallery, Route 117, Bolton, Massachusetts, USA.

Southgate Antique Auction Rooms, Rear of Town Hall, Green Lanes, Palmers Green, London N13.

Henry Spencer & Sons, 20 The Square, Retford, Nottinghamshire DN22 6DJ.

Stephenson & Son, 20 Castlegate, York YO1 1RT.

Street Jewellery, 16 Eastcliffe Avenue, Newcastle-upon-Tyne NE3 4SN.

G. E. Sworder & Sons, Northgate End Salerooms, 15 Northgate End, Bishops Stortford, Herts.

Taviner's of Bristol, Prewett Street, Redcliffe, Bristol BS1 6PB.

Tennants of Yorkshire, Old Chapel Saleroom, Market Place, Richmond, N. Yorkshire.

Thomson Roddick & Laurie, 60 Whitesands, Dumfries.

Tiffen King Nicholson, 12 Lowther Street, Carlisle, Cumbria CA3 8DA.

Duncan Vincent Fine Art & Chattel Auctioneers, 105 London Street, Reading RG1 4LF.

Wallis & Wallis, West Street Auction Galleries, West Street, Lewes, East Sussex BN7 2NJ.

Peter Wilson Fine Art Auctioneers, Victoria Gallery, Market Street, Nantwich, Cheshire.

H. C. Wolton & Son, 6 Whiting Street, Bury St Edmunds.

Woolley & Wallis, The Castle Auction Mart, Salisbury, Wiltshire SP1 3SU.

Contents

CONTENTS

Popular
ANTIQUES
and their Values
1875-1950

I n 1875 the style which we tend now to think of as typically Victorian was at its height. The Queen had been a widow for some thirteen years and as she settled back into gloom and heaviness, so too did these attributes characterise the furniture of the period, while elsewhere the vulgarly flamboyant decoration of everything from chamber pots to jewellery, went on unabated.

Even the most cursory glance through history will show the pendulum effect, or how one age reacts against another. The ponderous weight of much Victoriana can be seen as a reaction against the levity and frothiness which characterised the Regency, and by 1875 the pendulum was already beginning to swing back towards a simpler, more fluid style.

The products of William Morris had already been featured at the International Exhibition of 1862. Morris was co-founder of the furnishing firm of Morris, Marshall, Faulkner & Co, and came out strongly against the new mass production techniques, advocating a return to the pre-technology age of craftsmanship. Morris was closely connected with John Ruskin and the painters of the pre-Raphaelite Brotherhood, who idealised the medieval period, and who sought to emphasise a coherence and homogeneity between the decorative and structural elements of a piece. Ruskin and Morris favoured themes taken from nature, and extracted from natural forms those fluid linear motifs and plant shapes that were to be taken to

their furthest extremes by the practitioners of Art Nouveau.

'Peacock and Dragon', a pair of Morris and Co. woven twill curtains, the pale green, blue and terracotta twill woven with stylised peacock and dragon, 166 x 275cm.   *(Christie's) £1,078*

9

A Liberty & Co. oak and enamel mantel clock designed by Archibald Knox, the circular dial with a red scrolling design on a mottled blue and green ground, 29.3cm. high. (Christie's) £1,320

Another force pushing the pendulum back from Victorian fussiness was the fact that the Far East was rapidly being opened up for trade. The influence of bamboo and Japanese style prints and furniture with its minimal decoration and clear, straight lines, further fuelled the trend already begun by Morris and his friends.

The Art Nouveau movement was sponsored first in 1885 by the Liberty store in Regent Street, and the simple, flowing lines of the style, which could be translated into cloth, ornaments, furniture and jewellery, became instantly popular. The foundation of the Royal Academy of Art in London in 1851 had greatly increased public awareness of design, and by the 1880's its first students were established in positions from which they could influence the design of just about every marketable commodity.

In the illustrative arts, the Art Nouveau movement found one of its most devoted practitioners in Aubrey Beardsley, whose idealised images and stark lines were nevertheless totally at variance with the spirit of the pre-Raphaelites. Whereas their work had an open, almost angelic character, Beardsley's style was contrived and demoniacal, his pictures seeming to invite the spectator to abandon the restraint imposed by common sense and Victorian morality for a new life which would be free from bourgeois prejudices and would offer the most seductive prospects.

When Queen Victoria died, then, in 1901, she was already an anachronism. The outward trappings of the old era lingered to a degree through the reign of her son Edward VII, who, while his lifestyle might have been reminiscent of his great-uncle George IV, nevertheless lacked his artistic taste. The furniture known as Edwardian, though still often richly inlaid, was on the whole lighter and more delicate in form than its Victorian counterpart. Perhaps however the only antiques from that period which may owe something to the direct influence of Edward VII are the fishing rods, golf clubs, shotguns and billiard tables from the country house style of living popularised by the monarch.

An Edwardian mahogany and inlaid foldover top card table, on tapered legs with spade feet. (Phillips) £1,250

A Meissen group of the drunken Silenus, the scantily draped figure seated on a donkey supported by a standing, scantily draped figure, each wearing a wreath of fruiting-vine, circa 1880, 21cm. high. (Christie's) £440

William Morris had been a socialist, and this new doctrine was one which was gathering momentum throughout Europe. The Industrial Revolution had enriched some at the expense of others, while at the same time the availability of basic education for all had fuelled a thirst for knowledge among the downtrodden classes. Trade unions were organising as a result of this increased social awareness, and women too were embarking on their long quest for their basic rights. The world again was poised for change.

The change when it came was apocalyptic. With the Great War of 1914–18 British confidence was shattered and society changed for ever. Men from all classes were found to be truly equal in the ease with which they could die in the Flanders mud. Those who survived the holocaust were also fundamentally changed. Finding on their return that Britain was in no way a 'land fit for heroes to live in' as Lloyd George claimed, they set about reforming it, no longer content to be an exploited workforce, and they found their political voice in the Labour party.

The Elton suite of furniture by Heal & Son from their 1896 catalogue came in white, cream or any Art shade for just over £15 in total.

POPULAR ANTIQUES AND THEIR VALUES

The old way of life was vanishing too. Two million men, a vast percentage of the labour force, did not return. Few who did return, or their female counterparts, were now prepared to go back 'into service', when they could earn much more in commerce or industry. Costs rose too. Houses became smaller, and so, of course, did the furniture and artefacts which were to fill them. At the same time, a new flourishing technology also made labour saving devices more readily available to the housewife.

Throughout this period the Art Nouveau style gathered momentum. The Scottish architect Charles Rennie Mackintosh was designing buildings and furniture characterised by their long, vertical lines, while his wife Margaret often embellished the latter with decorations of flowers and flowing haired maidens. The period also saw the rise of the great artists in glass such as Tiffany, Gallé, Daum and Lalique, while in Germany Walter Gropius and the Bauhaus movement were to the fore.

A rare Galle mould-blown, double overlay and carved cala lily vase, signed, 35cm. high.
(Christie's Monaco)   £84,184

EDWARDIAN ROOM

In the early years of the twentieth century there was a movement of revolt against the Victorian tradition. This took the form of an art and craft movement led by William Morris, Charles Rennie Mackintosh and designers such as C. F. A. Voysey, whose products can be seen in the room opposite. Individually, many of the pieces from this period lack appeal but, seen as a complete room setting, they combine to create an air of artistic unity.

(Courtesy Geffrye Museum)

A Carlo Bugatti ebonised, inlaid and painted vellum table, the octagonal top with central vellum panel, painted with arabic script, 74cm. high.
(Christie's)   £7,480

13

A Clarice Cliff Fantasque applique Palermo pattern wall plate, 13in. diam. (Sworders) £3,000

One of a pair of Valabrega open armchairs, each back with central shaped, upholstered and braided panel within a curved, curvilinear, pierced framework.
(Christie's) £4,840

But the War, and perhaps too the subsequent Depression had had a deep effect on the emotional psyche of the country. The philosophy of 'carpe diem' inspired not just the Bright Young Things but the whole population. The survivors of the War danced to the new records that were being pressed, bought player pianos, phonographs, gramophones, cameras and cars. They found escapism in the cinema, experimented with cocktails and sponsored avant garde clothes designers. People wanted it all and they wanted it today. The gentle flowing lines of Art Nouveau were not for this generation. The bizarre and the outré were what counted and this found expression in the bright colours and sharp, angular patterns of the Art Deco style.

'The Sleep of Reason', cast from a model by Maurice Bouval, the dark patinated female figure with eyes closed, her hair bedecked with flowers, 43.5cm. high.
(Christie's) £1,980

Furniture in 'Weathered Oak' by Heal & Son, 1930. The 'Elysian' folding lounge chair, covered in corduroy, originally cost £5 while the hexagonal table was £8 and the rush seated chair £3.

A Pierre Perret ceramic wall pocket modelled as a pierrot's head, the border heightened in red, 25.3cm. diam. (Phillips) £150

Perhaps the last great invention pertaining to the world of household artefacts in the period covered by this book was bakelite. Discovered in 1909, it was used between the wars for a myriad of objects from radio cases to napkin rings. It led the field as a material for making inexpensive objects until the development of plastics in the 1960's, and is rapidly becoming a popular collecting field in its own right.

Up until very recently the period between the wars has been looked on as rather a stylistic desert, at any rate as far as furniture is concerned. China, pottery and glass of the period are already appreciated thanks to the work of such designers as Clarice Cliff, Suzie Cooper, Bernard Leach and others. However, as more and more items from the 30's and 40's are becoming collectable, the sign seen recently in an antique shop may be especially relevant 'The next person who comes in here and says "But my mother had one exactly the same as that" will be asked to leave'.

EELIN McIVOR

ADVERTISING SIGNS

Hall's Distemper. £120

Singer Sewing Machines.
£95

Nestle's Milk. £75

Martini. £85

Colman's Starch. £45

Phipp's 'Diamond Ale'. £110

Nectar Tea. £70

'Matchless' metal polish. £250

Shell. £40

Anti-Laria Sparkling Wine. £75

Tizer 'The Appetizer'. £40

Milkmaid Brand Milk. £200

Monsters. £125

Rowntree's Pastilles. £55

'Black Cat' Virginia Cigarettes. £175

Lucas 'Ace of Spades'. £150

Duckham's Oils. £75

Komo Metal Paste. £150

A rare advertising plaque by Mayer, printed in the style of Pratt, 'Rowland's Kalydor for the complexion', 6 x 8½in. £1,750

Faulkner's Sweet Rosemary Empire Grown Tobacco, printed tin sign, 22 x 43cm. £30

Enamel sign for Motorine Motor Oil, for longer, smoother, easier running. £150

Wincarnis, 'The World's Greatest Wine Tonic and Nerve Restorative', 72 x 40in. £500

Aladdin Liquid Metal Polish, 'Shines Brightest and Longest', 36 x 24in. £150

Quaker Oats, 40 x 26in. £350

Chocolat Menier 'Eviter Les Contrefacons', 24 x 10in. £250

Leica advertising poster, 27 x 34in., titled 'Leica', showing cutaway views of a Leica camera and a Hektor f 1.9 7.3cm. lens, 1930's. £132

Thorley's Food for Pigs, 28 x 18in. £100

Photographic advertisement for Continental Tyres featuring Boillot, winner of the Grand Prix, 1912.   £2,200

Nugget Boot Polish, tinplate counter display.   £75

Enamel sign for Raleigh, The Gold Medal Motor-Cycle.   £750

Enamel advertising sign, Good Year tyres.   £90

Painted and decorated trade sign, signed 'T. M. Woodward', Worcester, Massachusetts, circa 1875, the rectangular bowed metal panel painted dark green and decorated in polychrome, 48in. high. £22,857

R. Geri, 'Exide The Long Life Battery', showcard, 30 x 22in.   £50

Zebra Grate Polish, 36 x 24in.   £200

Fry's 'Five Boys' Chocolate, 24 x 36in.   £350

Enamel sign for Texaco Motor Oil, Drain, Flush and Refill.   £250

ALABASTER

Italian alabaster figure of a young child, late 19th century, crying over the injured bird in her hand, 21in. high. £419

An alabaster figure of a girl, carrying water pitchers, leaning against stone trough, signed Mozzanti, B, Florence, 62cm. high. £800

A carved alabaster bust of a curly-haired young man in the neo-Classical style, eyes incised, on turned socle, 58cm. high. £950

An early 20th century Florentine coloured alabaster bust, probably of Beatrice, from the workshop of Vichi, 11in. high. £440

A late 19th century alabaster portrait bust of Joan of Arc, wearing a laced-up bodice, signed F. Guerrieri, 39in. high. £385

A sculpted alabaster bust of a young woman, a scarf around her head, 13½in. high, on a stepped base. £250

An Italian alabaster lamp carved from a model by G. Gamboni as a mediaeval maiden in pleated robe, 32½in. high. £1,023

An Italian late 19th or early 20th century alabaster relief of a girl playing her violin, 38cm. high. £385

The Mermaid, a carved alabaster figure of a mermaid, by Sven Berlin, 24in. high. £1,650

20

AMUSEMENT MACHINES

Alwin de Luxe, British, 1935.
£200

Bonanza Jackpot, Thompson,
British, 1928.   £500

Bryan's Fruit Bowl, British,
1960's.   £160

Mills Extraordinary, USA,
1933.   £300

Roulette Visible, Buzzoz,
France, 1932.   £500

'Beat the Goalie', British,
1933.   £500

Circle Skill, British, 1928.
£275

British version of Caille
Pinwheel, Bollands, 1935.
£375

British version of Mills
Pinwheel, Clemence, 1935.
£375

AUTOMATONS

A clockwork musical automaton of a papier mache headed Japanese girl carrying tray and parasol, 33in. high, probably by Vichy. £4,950

A bisque headed clockwork clown standing on his hands dressed in original outfit, 16in. high. £350

A bisque headed musical automaton, modelled as a standing child holding a covered basket, 19in. high, by Lambert, the head stamped Tete Jumeau. £2,640

A clockwork automaton figure of a standing bear drummer, with moving lower jaw and front paws, 27in. high, probably Decamps, 1880. £1,100

A coin-in-the-slot automaton ship model, the three-masted vessel with all sail set, 42¾in. long. £1,550

A marotte with three dancing children with bisque heads and wooden bodies in original clothing, 11in. high (music needs attention). £410

A printed paper on wood automaton toy of a house on fire, with two figures working a pump at the side, 10in. high, German. £330

A very fine Gustav Vichy musical automaton of a young woman playing the guitar. £7,200

Brass singing bird automaton, having a pair of feathered model birds on branches under domed cage, 7in. high. £255

AUTOMATONS

A papier mache ginger jar musical automaton, French, late 19th century, the hinged cover opening to reveal a chinaman drinking tea, 12 in. high. £1,726

A musical automaton doll in the form of a magician linking together a long chain of brass rings, wearing an exotic costume in the Turkish style, 15¼ in. high. £940

A Leopold Lambert musical automaton of a flower girl, the Jumeau bisque head with fair mohair wig over cork pate, 18½ in. high. £3,400

A clockwork musical automaton of a papier mache headed North African girl, sitting on a stool inset with paste jewels and playing a lyre, 29 in. high. £4,180

SFBJ bisque headed automaton doll seated playing a piano, the doll impressed SFBJ 60 Paris, with brown hair and fixed brown glass eyes, 13½ in. wide. £400

An Armand Marseille bisque headed musical poupard, with blonde mohair wig, fixed blue glass eyes and open mouth, 38.5 cm. long overall. £400

The Reaper, a bisque headed clockwork musical automaton, modelled as a child in original red waistcoat, 17 in. high, by Vichy, the head stamped in red Tete Jumeau. £3,080

Celluloid singing bird in a painted tinplate cage, with clockwork mechanism in base of cage, 4¼ in. high, German, 1920's. £352

A bisque headed, hand operated automaton of a jester ringing handbells, dressed in original outfit, with musical movement, 15 in. high. £490

AUTOMOBILIA

Red and white cotton Bugatti driver's armband for the 1924 Grand Prix D'Europe. £500

A chromium plated and enamelled B.R.D.C. badge, stamped 767 Boshier-Jones, 4¼in. high. £280

'The Latest', 'Testing New Car for Width', by W. Heath Robinson, black ink, humorous cartoons, 2 x 5½in. Two £340

A petrol cigarette lighter modelled as the 1930 M.G. Midget, 6¼in. long. £290

A brass and cast two-note exhaust whistle, stamped Jubilee Horn No. 31, Boston, U.S.A., 12in. long. £85

Sir Malcolm Campbell's Bluebird, a clockwork tinplate toy by Kingsbury, repainted, £220

Frederick Nevin, Giuseppe Campari in his Alfa Romeo Monza, charcoal, heightened with white, signed, 15½x20½in. £275

Poster by Andre Bermond, for the Grand Prix Automobile, Pau, 10 Avril 1950, 39 x 30cm. £1,100

James Dugdale, 'Targa Florio 1964 Dan Gurney in the AC Cobra Campofelice', gouache, signed and dated 1980, 19½ x 22½in. £400

Frazer Nash Car Club badge. £160

A chromium plated Healey Car Club badge, 3¼in. high. £120

An enamelled convex Bugatti radiator badge, slight chip, 1¾ x 3½in. £120

Osterreichische Touren
Trophae 1931, Steinfellner, a
bronze plaque moulded in
relief with badge of the
Austrian Automobile Club,
3¾in. wide.   £60

Petrol pump globe for National
Benzole Mixture. Two   £180

Ferrari 275 GTB4, sales
pamphlet, Italian, French and
English text, 1964.   £187

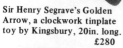

Sir Henry Segrave's Golden
Arrow, a clockwork tinplate
toy by Kingsbury, 20in. long.
£280

Bosch four cylinder magneto,
brass and steel advertising table
ornament, 3¼in. high.   £180

A chromium plated cigarette
lighter modelled as an MG
Midget, circa 1933, 6¼in. long.
£198

A pair of Lucas 'King of the
Road' headlamps, 8¾in. diam.,
and acetylene generator. £550

A sales brochure for Bentley
6½ Litre 6 Cylinder Standard
Model, catalogue no. 27,
October 1928.   £470

Petrol pump globe for Shell
Benzol Mixture.   £210

James Dugdale, 'Auto Union
C-Type cornering', gouache,
signed and dated 1980,
14 x 20in.   £450

A chromium plated and
enamelled Brooklands Automobile Racing Club badge,
stamped 419, 3¾in. high.
£450

After Gamy, 'Coupe des
Voitures Legeres 1911', Bablot
le Gagnant sur Delage.   £340

BRONZE

'Source d'Or', a bronze sculpture by Ernest Wante of a gold patinated maiden standing in a rocky enclave, 25.4cm. high. £880

A Tiffany Studios bronze candelabrum, with blown-out green Favrile glass in each holder, New York, 12in. high. £1,301

A late 19th/early 20th century bronze memorial relief, attributed to Sir Alfred Gilbert, 25cm. high. £330

'Bubble Dance', a bronze and ivory figure by A. Goddard, of Georgia Graves at the Folies Bergere, 1930, the female figure in short silver-patinated dress, 52.5cm. high. £6,050

'Les Amis de Toujours', a bronze and ivory figure by Demetre Chiparus, of a standing lady, flanked by two borzois, on a rectangular amber-coloured onyx base, 63cm. high. £13,200

'Skater', a silver-patinated bronze and ivory figure cast by Ferdinand Preiss, of a girl skating with one leg behind her, 33.4cm. high. £4,620

'The Strolling Minstrel', a bronze and ivory figure by Maurice Constant of a man dressed in mediaeval costume, 37cm. high. £440

'Cleopatra', a bronze figure by D. H. Chiparus, wearing a jewelled headdress, bodice and wrap skirt, 48cm. wide. £3,850

'Elegant', a gold patinated bronze and ivory group, cast and carved from a model by S. Bertrand, of a finely dressed woman standing with a greyhound at her side, 31.2cm. high. £2,200

BRONZE

Art Deco bronze and ivory figurine of a young woman on a jetty holding a canoe paddle. £2,200

A late 19th century Viennese bronze portrait bust of a young girl, cast from a model by Arthur Strasser, dated 1894, 42cm. high. £550

Wal Law 'The Left Winger'. A cast bronze of a footballer, signed, inscribed and dated 1929, 24in. high. £1,500

An early 20th century Swiss bronze statuette of a nude man hurling a rock entitled 'Der Steinstosser', cast from a model by Hugo Siegwart, 37cm. high. £1,760

'Speedskater', a bronze figure cast from a model by Carl Fagerberg of a racing skater, dated April 1932, 51.4cm. high. £2,200

A late 19th century French bronze statuette of 'L' Industrie Moderne', cast from a model by Charley Perron, 63cm. high. £495

A rare late 19th century English New Sculpture bronze statuette of Perseus, cast from a model by F.W. Pomeroy, 51cm. high. £13,200

A 19th century French bronze group of the Voyage of the Nations, cast from a model by Edouard Drouot, 49cm. high. £1,650

An early 20th century French bronze bust of Perseus, cast from a model by E. Hannaux, 56cm. high. £1,870

BRONZE

A Bergman 'Egyptianesque' gilt bronze female figure, she stands naked with her arms folded across her chest, £580

A fine bronze koro on tripod feet inlaid in iroe hirazogan and takazogan with bowing branches of wisteria, signed Ichiyosai Atsumitsu koku, late 19th century, 13cm. diam. £2,750

A cold painted bronze figure, attributed as a model by Colinet, of a naked girl with brown hair, poised above a stepped marble base, 49.5cm. high. £1,200

A bronze oviform vase modelled in relief with carp in swirling waters, signed Jounkoku, late 19th century, 22.5cm. high. £528

A pair of French bronze mid Eastern figures, after Jean Jules Salmson, circa 1900, a male with sword, pistols and wide brimmed hat, a female with water jug, 22½in. high. £1,065

L. & J. G. Stickley dinner gong, circa 1907, the arched frame supporting circular bronze gong, signed with Handcraft label, 33¾in. high. £4,857

'Gamin', a bronze and ivory figure by F. Preiss, of a girl dressed in a silver patinated short skirt suit, standing with her hands in her pockets, 34.3cm. high. £6,600

A bronze fish group cast from a model by E.Smith, and fashioned as fish swimming in unison perched on the crest of a wave, 27.5cm. £400

'Pitcher', a bronze figure cast from a model by Pierre Le Faguays, of a young girl in a short dress, 25cm. high. £286

BRONZE

A large patinated bronze figure cast from a model by Lorenzl of a semi naked dancing girl, 16¼in. high. £550

A bronze bust of a woman cast from a model by Dora Gordine, Paris, 1925, 36.8cm. high. £935

A gilt bronze and ivory figure of a young woman after Gregoire, 10in. high, signed, circa 1910. £1,350

A bronze figure by Cl. J. R. Colinet, modelled as a nude female standing on one foot, the other leg and both arms outstretched before her, supporting a ball on each, 26.7cm. high. £495

A bronze model of an elephant being attacked by two tigers, one crawling up its back, signed Seiya zo, late 19th century, 19cm. long . £385

'Fancy Dress', a cold-painted bronze and ivory group, cast and carved from a model by Demetre Chiparus, as a Pierrot wearing a green-silver costume dancing with his female companion, 48.5cm. high. £12,000

An early 20th century English bronze group of two naked youths playing leapfrog, by Arthur George Walker R.A., 31cm. high. £660

A 20th century bronze model of a turtle, after Giovanni Antoniati, piped to emit water through mouth, 89 x 61cm. £1,650

'The Waiter', a bronze figure cast from a model by Engelhart of a waiter in tailcoat carrying dishes, dated 1904, 26.6cm. high. £220

BRONZE

'Dancer with Ring', a bronze and ivory figure by D. H. Chiparus, of an oriental dancing girl wearing a jewelled headdress, 46.5cm. high. £13,200

'Penthesilia, Queen of the Amazons', a bronze figure cast from a model by A. Bouraine, 48.2cm. long. £880

A late 19th century French bronze bust of a young cavalier, cast from a model by Ernest Rancoulet, 66cm. high. £770

'Moth Girl', a bronze and ivory figure by Ferdinand Preiss, of a girl standing on tiptoe and examining a glass over her shoulder, 41.6cm. high. £4,950

An early 20th century French bronze statuette of a naked woman, known as 'La Verite Meconnue', after Aime Jules Dalou, 22.5cm. high. £1,026

A mechanical bronze figure cast after a model by C. Kauba, on a square bronze base, circa 1920, 21cm. high. £756

Bronze bust of 'Dalila', by E. Villanis, circa 1890, seal of Societe des Bronzes de Paris. £900

An early 20th century German or French bronze group of Saint George on horseback, 55.5 x 36cm. £550

A late 19th century French bronze group of a huntsman holding aloft a dead partridge , cast from a model by Paul Delabrierre, 53cm. high. £1,650

30

BRONZE

A late 19th or early 20th century Austrian bronze statuette of a huntsman, cast from a model by H. Muller, wearing traditional hunting clothing, 45cm. high. £308

A gilt bronze tray cast from a model by Maurice Bouval, formed as a leaf with the figure of a nymph holding flowers, signed M. Bouval, 17.5cm. high. £715

An early 20th century Austrian bronze bust of Edward VII, cast from a model by J. Muhr, dated 1908, 40cm. high. £825

An Anglo-Australian early 20th century bronze figure of Diana wounded, cast from a model by Sir Bertram Mackennal, 42cm. high overall. £8,800

A late 19th or early 20th century French bronze group of a walking cow with a peasant girl knitting beside it, cast from a model by J. Garnier, 22.5 x 25cm. £495

'Golfer', a bronze and ivory figure, by D. H. Chiparus, of a girl swinging a golf club and wearing a green-patinated skirt, 36.8cm. high. £9,900

A rare early 20th century English bronze statuette of the Spirit of Ecstasy, cast from a model by Charles Sykes, 60cm. high. £5,500

An early 20th century Belgian bronze bust of a stevedore, cast from a model by Constantin Meunier, inscribed Anvers, 58cm. high. £3,520

'Exotic Dancer', a gold-patinated bronze and ivory figure by Gerdago of a female dancer making a theatrical curtsey, 30.5cm. high. £13,200

CADDIES & BOXES

An oblong chased silver gilt singing bird box, circa 1900, 4½in. long. £941

A French tortoiseshell and enamel singing bird box, circa 1900, 4in. long. £1,257

An oblong enamelled gilt singing bird box, circa 1900, 4in. long. £1,344

An extensive Art Deco cased silver and enamelled toilet set, made by the Goldsmiths and Silversmiths Co. Ltd., all in blue crocodile leather case, 45cm. wide, London 1934. £2,000

A travelling dressing set with silver mounts, dated 1901, Birmingham, in an alligator skin case. £420

A wooden, painted gesso and gilded casket, by W. Cayley-Robinson, 35cm. wide. £850

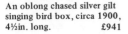

Victorian oak cased smoker's companion with earthenware tobacco jar and plated brass fittings. £100

Late 19th century mahogany slide cabinet of twenty-one drawers, containing slides by various makers, 12in. high. £715

An Edwardian tortoiseshell tea caddy in the form of a knife box, with silver banding and escutcheon, Birmingham Assay 1909, 10cm. £620

CADDIES & BOXES

A rosewood portable writing desk with countersunk brass handles, late Regency period, 14in. wide. £280

An early 19th century Anglo-Indian vizagapatam ivory and ebony games box, 18in. wide. £1,296

A miniature Tunbridgeware cabinet with domed top and hinged door, 18cm. wide, 15cm. high. £200

A late 19th century rectangular tabako-bon decorated in gold and silver hiramakie, hirame and heidatsu on a yasuriko ground, 20.5cm. wide. £702

A Victorian brass and velvet 'perambulator' sewing box, possibly America, circa 1880, 7½in. long. £258

Late 19th century roironuri two-tiered covered box, unsigned, School of Zeshin. 24.2 x 19.7 x 19.2cm. £1,512

A Victorian 12in. rectangular coromandel wood and brass bound vanity case, maker's mark J.V. £300

An Edwardian marquetry writing compendium with folding writing slope and fitted interior, 12in. wide. £400

A French red tortoiseshell and boulle decanter box, the lock stamped Jean A Rennes, late 19th century, 14½in. wide. £990

CAMERAS

C. P. Goerz, 16mm. Minicord camera no. 7164 with a Goerz, Wien Helgar f 2 2.5cm. lens. £242

Newman and Guardia, quarter plate 'Nydia' camera no. 463 with a Ross, London symmetric Anastigmat 5½in., f 8 lens. £308

J. Richard, rare 35mm. 80 x 30mm. stereoscopic 'Homeos' camera no. 291 with a pair of Kraus/Zeiss Tessar f 4.5 28mm. lenses. £1,430

W. I. Chadwick, half plate brass and mahogany stereoscopic camera with a pair of brass bound lenses with wheel stops barrels. £550

H. Ernemann, Dresden, 9 x 12cm. tropical Heag II/II camera with tan coloured bellows, brass fittings and polished wood body. £715

Marion and Co., good and rare 1½ x 1½in. Academy camera in polished mahogany and brass fittings with plate holder and viewfinder. £3,520

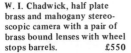

Thornton-Pickard 4.5 x 6cm. Snappa camera with lens front panel marked 'Pat. No.26186 11'. £242

A Le Coultre Et Cie, Compass camera No. 2325 with a CCL 35mm. f 3.5 Anastigmat lens, all contained within a fitted pigskin case. £715

A Dollond half plate studio camera, the lens with irised diaphragm, f8 to f64, together with three mahogany double sided plate holders, £132

CAMERAS

A 3¼ x 4¼ in. mahogany sliding box wet plate camera stamped 402 with a brass bound portrait lens. £792

Newman and Guardia, very rare 116 film 'Special stereoscope roll film Sibyl' camera No. A729 with a pair of Ross, London patent Xpres 75mm. f 4.5 lenses. £1,210

Horne & Thornthwaite, rare and unusual 6½ x 7½in. mahogany collapsible camera with brass fittings. £7,150

A quarter plate mahogany 'Loman's Patent Reflex Camera' with a brass bound Loman & Co., Amsterdam lens with rack and pinion focusing. £1,045

A Henry Park plate brass and mahogany tailboard camera with a brass bound Emil Busch rapid aplanat 10in. f 8 lens. £94

A twin lens Contaflex camera with a Zeiss Sucher-Objectiv f 2.8 8cm. viewing lens. £935

A rare quarter plate wooden bodied twin lens reflex camera with six integral mahogany double dark slides, maker's plaque 'H Park, Manufacturer'. £825

Mashpriborintorg, Narciss camera No. 6501138 with a Vega-M-1 f 2.8 35mm. lens. £440

W. Butcher and Sons, 3¼ x 4¼in. 'Royal Mail' camera with fifteen lenses mounted in five rows of three set into a simple shutter. £605

CAR MASCOTS

A chromium plated Rolls-Royce Spirit of Ecstasy, signed Charles Sykes, circa 1925, 5½in. high. £143

'Cinq Chevaux', a Lalique moulded glass car mascot, commissioned by Citroen in 1925, modelled as the overlapping bodies of five spirited horses, 11.5cm. high. £3,600

A nickel plated baby's dummy, marked REG, circa 1926, 3½in. long. £308

A brass Felix the Cat, 1930's, 4in. high. £198

'Faucon', a Lalique car mascot, the amethyst tinted clear and satin finished glass with traces of black staining, moulded as a falcon, 15.5cm. high. £990

A nickel plated Vauxhall griffin, the base stamped Joseph Fray Ltd., Birmingham, circa 1930, 3¼in. high. £187

'Grenouille', a Lalique moulded glass car mascot, modelled as a small frog in crouched position, 5.8cm. high. £8,200

A brass dragonfly, the base stamped M. Bertin, circa 1920, 6½in. high. £242

A chromium plated Humber stylised horse on stepped base, circa 1935, 5¼in. high. £143

AMERICAN

A large cobalt decorated stoneware pitcher, Pennsylvania, late 19th century, salt glazed baluster form, 11in. high.£369

Two Cowan pottery figural candlesticks, Cleveland, Ohio, 1925, depicting beavers, 9¾in. high. £242

A Jervis Art pottery motto mug, 1906, 5¾in. high, 4in. diam. £119

A Tiffany Art pottery vase, New York, 1906, of cylindrical form with repeating moulded lady slippers on stems, 12¼in. high. £2,142

Twelve handpainted porcelain plates, 1901, by Ella J. Libby, with shaped edge painted with seaweed and seashells, 9in. diam. £342

A Shawsheen pottery vase, probably Billerica, circa 1906, 6in. high. £119

An incised salt glazed stoneware presentation pitcher, attributed to Richard C. Remmy, Philadelphia, Pennsylvania, circa 1880, 10½in. high. £2,729

A 19th century glaze and slip decorated redware platter, New England, 13½in. long. £1,625

Hampshire pottery vase, Keene, New Hampshire, circa 1900, with repeating moulded tulip and running stem decoration, 9in. high. £200

CHINA

BELLEEK

Belleek cream-ground shaped handled jug, black factory mark 'Robinson & Cleaver, Belfast', circa 1935.   £180

Belleek strapwork porcelain basket with impressed Belleek mark to base, approximately 9 x 6in.   £120

Late 19th century Belleek figure of a young lady dressed in a classical style pink robe, 14¼in. high.   £780

BERLIN

A Berlin plaque painted after Raphael with a detail of the 'Madonna di San Sisto', late 19th century, 25.5 x 19cm.   £935

Late 19th century Berlin bowl and cover, blue sceptre mark, 10.5in. diam.   £600

A Berlin oval plaque painted after A. Kauffmann with a Vestal Virgin, impressed KPM, scepter, F and 5 marks, late 19th century, 27cm. high.   £1,540

BORNE

A Daisy Borne pottery group, modelled as a mother, sitting naked to the waist on a pedestal base, 29.3cm. high. £200

A pottery figure of a mermaid, attributed to Daisy Borne, modelled as a naked female figure kneeling on a base of sea-shells and waves, 27cm. high.   £160

A large pottery figure of a mermaid, attributed to Daisy Borne, she emerges from a wave-decorated base, embellished with fish, 29cm. high.   £300

38

BRITISH

A large pottery 'Egyptian-esque' jardiniere, the design attributed to Christopher Dresser and Bretby, having twin-fluted handles, 38.5cm. high. £360

A Brownfield jug modelled as a cockatoo, standing on logs, his crest forming the spout, 24.6cm. high. £388

A majolica glazed Stilton cheese dish and cover, probably by George Jones & Sons, late 19th century. £85

A flambe pottery bowl, by Bernard Moore, 8¼in. diam., and a Chinese carved wood stand. £230

An underglaze coloured Toby jug of Winston Churchill, by 'Wilton Pottery of Cobridge', 17cm. high. £60

A Crown Ducal 'Manchu' pattern bowl, designed by Charlotte Rhead, 25.5cm. diam. £95

An earthenware handbuilt coiled amphora vase with two loop handles, by Fiona Salazar, circa 1984, 28cm. high. £200

Edwardian china biscuit barrel with plated mounts. £20

An H. J. Wood Bursley Ware vase, slip-trailed and coloured 'Seed-Poppy' design, circa 1930-5, 12in. high. £70

BRITISH

A George Jones 'Majolica' game tureen, cover and liner, with a frieze of fern and stiff leaves in shades of green on a dark brown ground, circa 1880, 28cm. wide. £308

A Brannam pottery figure of a standing frog holding a giant lily leaf, in shades of blue and green, 12¼in. high. £550

A majolica tazza, England, with Art Nouveau poly-chrome iris decoration, circa 1900, 9¼in. diam. £91

Late 19th century pottery biscuit barrel with floral decoration and plated mounts. £20

A tin glazed earthenware ewer and two of eight goblets, by A. Caiger-Smith, date cypher for 1983, ewer 28.1cm. high. £151

A Morrisware pear-shaped vase painted with mauve flowerheads and green foliage on a blue ground, 11in. high. £220

A globular green glazed bowl designed by Dr. C. Dresser, 14.5cm. high. £561

A Beswick pottery wall mask modelled as the face of a young woman, 9½in. high. £165

An unusual china chamber pot, circa 1940, the inside base with cartoon head of Hitler, inscription round brim "Have this on 'old nasty' another violation of 'Poland'." £180

40

CARDEW

A large stoneware teapot by Michael Cardew with strap handle and grip, Wenford Bridge seals, circa 1970, 23.4cm. high. £638

An earthenware coffee pot by Michael Cardew, covered in a pale brown glaze over which pale yellow, stopping short of the foot, 14.8cm. high. £176

A large 'Gwari' stoneware casserole by Michael Cardew, covered in a translucent mottled olive brown and green glaze, 26.5cm. high. £935

An earthenware inscribed platter by Michael Cardew, decorated by Henry Bergen, Winchcombe Pottery seals, 42.7cm. diam £1,100

A large stoneware jar by Seth Cardew, the cylindrical body with four strap handles to the shoulder, 61.8cm. high. £308

A stoneware plate by Seth Cardew, impressed SC and Wenford Bridge seals, 35.6cm. diam. £143

An earthenware cider flagon by Michael Cardew, circa 1970, 41cm. high. £440

An Abuja large deep bowl on shallow foot, 34cm. wide. £154

An earthenware cider flagon by Michael Cardew, with olive-brown brushwork bands of stylised foliage, impressed MC and Winchcombe Pottery seals. 25.4cm. high £416

CARLTON WARE

A Carlton ware orange ground bowl boldly decorated with flowers and multi-patterned quarter circle motifs, 9½in. diam. **£110**

A Carlton Ware Limited Edition punch bowl, moulded in relief with a frieze of Henry VIII, his wives and children, 21cm. high. **£340**

A Carltonware rouge royale diamond-shaped dish with two 'fin' handles, 12in.wide. **£15**

A Carltonware oviform ginger jar and cover, painted with clusters of stylised flowerheads and bold geometric bands, 31cm. high. **£1,080**

Carlton Ware lustre jug with gilt loop handle, the body painted and gilded with stylised floral and fan decoration, 5in. high. **£115**

One of a pair of Carltonware vases, 21cm. high, and a tray, 25cm. wide. **£540**

A highly unusual Carlton ware ceramic butter dish depicting a well proportioned couple in horizontal embrace, 26cm. across. **£360**

A Carlton Ware pottery advertising lampbase made for Guinness, 9½in. high. **£176**

A Carltonware plaque painted in gilt, orange, blue, green and white with wisteria and exotic plants, 15½in. diam. **£200**

CHINA

CHALKWARE

Late 19th century painted chalkware horse, 10in. high.
£161

A pair of late 19th century painted chalkware doves, American, 11½in. high.
£297

A 19th century painted chalkware cat, America, 10¾in. high.
£505

CHELSEA KERAMIC

Late 19th century Chelsea Keramic Art Works pottery 'oxblood' vase, 8in. high.
£1,190

Late 19th century Chelsea Keramics Art Works pottery vase, Mass., 10½in. high.
£1,428

Late 19th century Chelsea Keramic Art Works covered jar, Mass., impressed CKAW, 5½in. high.
£90

CHINESE

A rose Mandarin punch bowl, China, late 19th century, deep bowl decorated with colourful alternating panels, 15¾in. diam.
£909

One of a pair of 19th century rose medallion garden seats, China, 19in. high.
£3,671

An export "Blue Fitzhugh" basin, China, late 19th century, the interior decorated with central medallion, 15¾in. wide.
£625

CLARICE CLIFF

An unusual Clarice Cliff cat, naturalistically modelled with smiling expression and wearing a green bow-tie, 15.7cm. high. £900

A Clarice Cliff Bizarre biscuit barrel and cover, painted with a band of stylised fruit and foliage, 6in. high. £242

Clarice Cliff; a good sugar dredger, the ribbed body decorated with trees and flowers, 5in. high. £60

'Tulip' a Clarice Cliff Lotus vase, with ribbed relief signed Cafe-au-Lait, Hand-Painted Bizarre by Clarice Cliff, Newport Pottery, England, 30cm. high. £1,045

An "Inspiration" Clarice Cliff charger, decorated on a turquoise cloud ground with a knight on horseback, 18in. diam. £2,800

A large Clarice Cliff 'Churchill' Toby Jug, inscribed on base 'Going into Action, May God Defend the Right', 30.5cm. high, signed 'Clarice Cliff' No. 292'. £1,760

A Clarice Cliff Bizarre pottery mask, kite-shaped, 28cm. long. £1,100

A Clarice Cliff Bizarre oviform jug in the 'Snake Tree' pattern, 6¾in. high. £350

Clarice Cliff; a turquoise ground female nymph wall vase, 9½in. high. £250

CLIFTON

A Clifton Art pottery 'Indian Ware' vase, circa 1910, 8in. high, 10in. diam.   £193

Clifton Indianware pottery vase, New Jersey, circa 1907, 12in. high. £200

A Clifton Art pottery 'Indian Ware' vase, circa 1910, 10½in. high, 12in. diam.   £178

COALPORT

A Coalport jewelled box and cover modelled as a pair of bellows, enamelled in colours in imitation of opalescent stone and gilt with a floral motif reserved on a gold ground, circa 1894, 23.5cm. long.   £550

A pair of Coalport jewelled miniature ewers, enamelled with turquoise beading on gold grounds, the cream-ground shoulders with a band of gilt and red jewelled ornament, circa 1890, 7in. high.   £550

1897 Jubilee: A Coalport plate printed in blue with a statue and commonwealth members, cracked.   £30

COMMEMORATIVE

1902 Coronation: A Wedgwood plate printed in blue with portrait and the Dominions.   £75

1935 Silver Jubilee of George V: A Wedgwood jug with floral description and inscription in black, 20cm. high.   £100

A plate printed in black with portraits inscribed to commemorate the Royal Visit to Canada in 1901.   £50

COMMEMORATIVE

A tapering mug printed in black with a portrait of Victoria inscribed *'Liverpool Shipperies Exhibition, Opened...May 11th, 1886'*. £130

1888 Silver Wedding of the Prince and Princess of Wales, a Doulton stoneware three handled loving cup. £220

Edward VIII: A Crown Ducal pottery jug with Art Nouveau decoration, inscribed below *'Rhead'*, 19cm. high. £45

An octagonal plate printed in black within a thistle border 'Royal visit to Burnley - Opened Victoria Hospital Oct. 13th 1886'. £180

Death of Edward VII: A Doulton Lambeth statue on blue base 1910. £190

1937 Coronation: A Crown Ducal pottery plate decorated in Art Nouveau style in blue, orange and gold. £45

Edward VIII: A green jug with portrait and flags printed in colours, inscribed below *'Abdicated Dec. 11th, 1936'*. £160

Death of Edward VII: A plate printed in blue with portrait, with raised decorative border, chipped. £30

Death of Edward VII: A jug printed in black, inscribed with dates on the reverse. £40

CHINA

COPELAND

Late 19th century Copeland ironstone canted rectangular carving dish with gravy well, 21¼in. wide. £120

A Copeland 'orchid' vase, painted by T. Sadler, signed and dated 1904, 62.5cm. high. £1,000

A Copeland circular wall plaque, painted by R. R. Tomlinson, with a winged figure standing over a kneeling man, 47.5cm. diam., dated 1908. £170

COPER

A stoneware 'spade' form by Hans Coper, the gently swollen compressed body on cylindrical base, incised with spiral decoration, impressed HC seal, circa 1967, 27.4cm. high. £11,000

A small stoneware sack-form with spherical belly by Hans Coper, covered in a bluish-buff slip, burnished and textured to reveal areas of matt-manganese, impressed HC seal, circa 1969, 14.8cm. high. £4,620

A waisted cylindrical stoneware vase by Hans Coper, impressed HC seal, circa 1957, 18.6cm. high. £1,320

A rare early stoneware shallow dish by Hans Coper, covered in a matt manganese glaze, impressed HC seal, circa 1950, 37cm. diam. £20,900

An early small stoneware bowl by Hans Coper, with undulating rim, circa 1955, 14cm. diam. £4,950

A stoneware black bulbous bottle, by Hans Coper, circa 1965, 14.7cm. high. £6,050

CRESTED CHINA

Lion inscribed 'King of the Forest', by Swan, 105mm. long. £20

Bust of a clown, 80mm. high, by Arcadian, inscribed 'Put me amongst the girls'. £20

An Arcadian model of despatch rider on motorbike, 120mm. long. £50

Sir John Franklin Memorial, 150mm. high, by Willow Art. £100

Arcadian boy and girl sitting on a log, 90mm. long, some colouring. £60

Policeman with raised hand, 140mm. by Carlton. £50

'Scotch and Soda' bottles on horse-shoe base, 85mm. long, by Willow. £18

Battleship H.M.S. Tiger by Carlton, 170mm. long. £85

Podmore Sack of Coal, 95mm. some colouring. £20

DE MORGAN

A William de Morgan ruby lustre charger, decorated with a peacock, circa 1900, 36cm. diam. £550

A William de Morgan bowl, painted in red lustre with a stylised design of fish against a scrolling foliage pattern, 25cm. diam. £880

A De Morgan charger, decorated by Chas. Passenger, 1890's, 41.5cm. diam. £7,150

A William de Morgan tile, painted in red lustre with two stylised carnations, with painted signature W. de Morgan & Co., Fulham, London, 20.5 x 20.5cm. £165

A William de Morgan vase decorated by Joe Juster, bulbous form with cylindrical neck, painted in red, pink and gold lustre with birds amid stylised foliage, 25.3cm. high. £1,430

A William de Morgan tile, square, painted in red lustre with a hippocampus on a white ground, impressed W. de Morgan on reverse (1872-1881), 20 x 20cm. £264

A William de Morgan charger, decorated by Charles Passenger, painted in red and grey lustre with swans amid foliage, 40cm. diam. £1,430

A William de Morgan lustre vase, painted in ruby tones against white with serpents, 16cm. high. £950

A William de Morgan lustre dish, painted in ruby lustre, pink and vivid mustard tones, 36cm. diam. £2,300

CHINA

EDHAM

Early 20th century Dedham pottery crackleware vase, decorated with white iris on blue ground, signed, 7½in.
£1,189

A Dedham pottery elephant charger, Mass., circa 1929, 12in. diam.
£750

Early 20th century Dedham pottery crackleware vase, decorated with blue iris, 7in.
£297

Dedham pottery polar bear plate, circa 1929-1943, stamped and the word 'Registered', 7in. diam.
£271

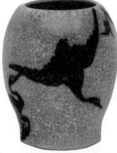

Early 20th century Dedham pottery decorated crackleware vase, 7½in. high.
£1,190

Early 20th century Dedham pottery plate with Fairbanks house, 8½in. diam.　£1,833

A Dedham Pottery covered Scottie dog jar, Dedham, Massachusetts, early 20th century, depicting three Scottie dogs (repaired), 6in. high.　£685

Early 20th century Dedham pottery large milk pitcher, Rabbit pattern, 8½in. high.
£227

Early 20th century Dedham crackleware metal shape vase, 8½in. high.　£769

DELLA ROBBIA

A Della Robbia vase of swollen cylindrical shape with flaring cylindrical neck, incised Della Robbia mark and decorators' monogram, 22.2cm. high. £100

'Water Avens Tile', a Della Robbia tile panel designed by Conrad Dressler and decorated by E. M. Wood, 51.5 x 34.2cm. £605

A Della Robbia twin-handled vase, decorated by Liz Wilkins, with incised and slip decoration of daffodils framed by a leafy pattern, 41.3cm. high. £660

A Della Robbia vase decorated by Charles Collis, with an incised frieze of running hounds against a background suggesting grassy slopes with trees, 32.5cm. high. £462

A Della Robbia twin-handled vase, decorated by Charles Collis, with eight circular medallions, each with a sea-creature whose long tail curls round on itself, 35.8cm. high. £660

'The Third Day of Creation', a Della Robbia tile panel after a design by Edward Burne-Jones, 55.5 x 21.5cm. £2,860

A Della Robbia wall charger, the base incised DR with a sailing ship and artist's monogram, 47.5cm. diam. £378

A Della Robbia pottery vase by Roseville Pottery, signed with Rozane Ware seal, circa 1906, 8¼in. high. £590

A Della Robbia jardiniere, bulbous shape with incised and slip decoration of a scrolling foliate band between foliate rim and foot borders, 25.6cm. high. £600

'Votes for Women', a Royal Doulton stoneware figural inkwell, designed by Leslie Harradine, 9cm. high.
£420

A Royal Doulton 'Sung' bowl, decorated with a central leaping deer amongst foliage with a spiral and diamond design, 13in. diam. £440

A Doulton Lambeth stoneware cricketing jug, decorated in Art Nouveau taste with applied figures of cricketers, 15cm. high. £260

A Royal Doulton Limited Edition Tower of London jug. £450

Pair of Doulton Faience vases, dated 1885, 9½in. high. £200

A Doulton, Burslem, ovoid vase, the panel painted by Fred Sutton, 17cm. high.
£400

'The Coming of Spring', HN1723, designed by L. Harradine, introduced 1935, withdrawn 1949, 12.5in. high.
£500

'Brown-Haired Clown', a Royal Doulton character jug, large, D5610, designed by H. Fenton, introduced 1937, withdrawn 1942. £1,050

'The Wandering Minstrel' HN1224, designed by L. Harradine, introduced 1927, withdrawn 1938, 7in. high.
£850

DOULTON

A Doulton Lambeth globular vase, by William Parker, carved with panels depicting classical warriors, 20.9cm. high. **£190**

A Doulton Lambeth faience circular wall plaque, painted with a head and shoulders of a red haired girl dressed in turquoise, 43.7cm. diam. **£320**

Doulton Lambeth stoneware tobacco jar and cover with applied Art Nouveau decoration, 6in. high, circa 1925. **£75**

Doulton Lambeth stoneware jug decorated with bacchanalian figures and verse, circa 1895, 7in. high. **£105**

A pair of Doulton Art Nouveau stoneware vases by Frank Butler, each damaged, 18½in. high. **£320**

A Doulton Lambeth stoneware vase by Francis C. Pope, 16½in. high, impressed and incised artist monogram. **£352**

'Young Miss Nightingale', HN2010, a Royal Doulton figure designed by M. Davies, 9½in. high. **£330**

Royal Doulton character jug, 'Old King Cole', with yellow crown and grey/white hair, 6in. high. **£3,300**

Royal Doulton figure, 'Harlequinade', HN585. **£400**

CHINA

DRESDEN

A Dresden clockcase of arch form on three high scroll feet, surmounted by a putto emblematic of Autumn, circa 1880, 48cm. high.   £825

A 'Dresden' large group of 'La Fete des Bonnes Gens' after the Sevres biscuit original, circa 1880, 43cm. wide.   £1,760

A Dresden baluster vase and cover, painted with lovers at pastimes in landscape vignettes, late 19th century, 46cm. high.   £462

EUROPEAN

Early 20th century Gouda pottery covered urn, Holland, 16½in. high.   £238

A Goebel Art Deco ceramic figural group moulded as three dancing girls leaning forwards, 11½in. high.   £1,012

A Wiener Keramik figure of a putto, designed by M. Powolny, 40.5cm. high.   £2,160

An Orchies pottery figure, designed by Dax, 13¼in. high, printed and painted marks   £95

A Massier art pottery jardiniere, sculpted to simulate ocean waves with a full-form nude woman perched amidst the breakers, 9½in. high.   £1,715

A Rozenburg egg-shell square-shaped vase painted with blue and green stylised foliage on a white ground, 11in. high.   £720

FOLEY

A Foley 'Pastello' earthenware vase of flattened
globular shape, England,
circa 1900, 16.5cm. high.
£300

A Foley Intarsio pottery vase,
with panels of foliage alternating with panels of seagulls,
22cm. high.　　　£150

A Foley Intarsio oval teapot
and cover printed and painted
to represent a bald gentleman
with beard, 8in. wide.　£352

A Foley 'Intarsio' earthenware vase of ovoid shape
with two handles, England,
circa 1900, 26cm. high.
£450

A Foley Intarsio ceramic clock,
painted in blue, turquoise, green,
brown and yellow enamels, with
Art Nouveau maidens representing day and night, 29cm. high.
£825

A Foley 'Intarsio' tobacco
jar and cover, 14.3cm. high,
no. 3458, Rd. no. 364386
(SR).　　　　　£140

A Foley Intarsio circular
wall plate, designed by
Frederick Rhead, the centre
with two classical maidens
seated on a garden bench,
36.8cm.diam.　£800

Early 20th century Arts &
Crafts ceramic umbrella stand,
stamped with logo, 'The Foley
"Intarsio" England', 27½in.
high.　　　　£416

A set of six Foley bone china
plates designed by Laura Knight,
A.R.A., painted with two
golden-haired young women
picking fruit in colours and
copper lustre, 21.5cm. diam.,
£900

A Max Lauger pottery jug, decorated in slip with green wind blown tulip-like flowers against a deep-blue ground, 24cm. high. £300

A 19th century Samson porcelain figure of Minerva, approx. 15in. high. £210

A French earthenware ornamental circular plaque, signed Belet, circa 1880-1900. £125

Late 19th century Lachenal Art pottery pitcher, French, 15¾in. high. £238

A Limoges teaset for six, the whole covered in a mauve glaze, comprising teapot, hot water jug, sugar bowl and cover, milk jug, six cups and saucers, teapot 9¼in. high. £264

A Primavera pottery figure depicting a female in broadly flared pantaloons, 29cm. high, stamped 'Primavera, France', signed Levy. £130

A Galle faience model of a cat, the smiling creature painted with blue and white circular and heart shaped motifs reserved against a yellow ground, 32.2cm. high. £380

A Haviland art pottery vase by Chaplet, of red clay with whimsical sgraffito decoration of a young fisherman, 11¼in. high. £650

An Art Deco porcelain spirit flask and stopper, 'Joueur de Golfeur', 27.5cm. high. £270

GARDNER

A porcelain biscuit figure of a street vendor, by the Gardner Factory (impressed mark), circa 1885, 4¾in. high. £385

A porcelain figure of a blind beggar, by the Gardner Factory (red printed and impressed marks), circa 1885, 6¼in. high. £352

A porcelain group of a mother and child, by the Gardner Factory (impressed mark), circa 1885, 17.2cm. high.   £440

A porcelain biscuit figure of an ice breaker, by the Gardner Factory (red printed and impressed mark), circa 1885, 11½in. high.   £385

A porcelain biscuit group of Gogol's Dead Souls, portraying Chichikov haggling with two men, by the Gardner Factory, circa 1885, 5½in. high. £935

A porcelain biscuit figure of a Mezienskii Samoyed, by the Gardner Factory (red printed mark), circa 1885, 9¼in. high.   £275

A porcelain biscuit group of a child seated on a trestle (hands repaired) and another playing a horn, by the Gardner Factory, circa 1885, 4¾in. high. £286

A porcelain figure of a peasant eating lunch, by the Gardner Factory (red impressed mark), circa 1885, 4½in. high. £528

A porcelain biscuit figure of a peasant, seated on a bench, by the Gardner Factory (impresses mark), circa 1885, 14cm. high.   £605

GERMAN

Pair of Sitzendorf figurines, depicting flower girl and gardener boy, impress marks to base 'S' 'DEP' '15024', circa 1880. £140

A Wiener Keramik ceramic wall-mask, moulded as a girl's head with a hat, painted in polychrome glazes, 24cm. high. £605

Late 19th century pair of German porcelain figures, a dandy fruit gatherer with his female companion, 12in. tall. £200

An Art Deco Rosenthal figure of a young girl running with a leaping fawn to the base, 12in. £500

A pair of German porcelain figures of nodding Mandarins, modelled as a man and a woman seated cross-legged, late 19th century, about 30cm. high. £1,870

Late 19th century German figure of a monkey, decorated in grey and yellow glazes, 46cm. high. £440

A Sitzendorf pierced circular basket, the scroll base with three figures of cupids holding flowers, 31cm. high. £374

A German plaque by Louis Renders, after David Neal, with Mary Queen of Scots' first encounter with Rizzio, signed, circa 1887, 29 x 21.5cm. £660

A large German Modernist ceramic group modelled as a warrior astride a large rearing horse emerging from the waves, 44cm. high. £320

GOLDSCHEIDER

A Goldscheider ceramic wall mask fashioned as the face of a girl with black eyes and orange lips, 28.5cm. high. £400

A Goldscheider figure, of a dancing girl in bodice and split skirt which she holds out behind her, enamelled in pink and cerise, 27.1cm. high. £750

A Goldscheider ceramic wall mask modelled as the head of a girl with turquoise eyes and orange lips, 27cm. high. £280

A Goldscheider Art Deco female child figure wearing a cape and a bonnet 'The New Gloves', 8in. high. £290

An unusual Goldscheider pottery group, modelled as a group of men, wearing colourful medieval style clothes, holding a large metal and ceramic spear, 49cm. long. £300

An Art Deco Goldscheider pottery figure designed by Dakon, modelled as a girl holding a large pink fan in front of her naked body, 33cm. high. £520

A Goldscheider figure, the design by J. Lorenzl, of a striding girl, her head thrown back, and holding her grey dress behind her, 35.4cm. high. £550

A Goldscheider pottery figure designed by Lorenzl, the standing young woman holding butterfly wings, 11½in. high. £1,045

A Goldscheider figure, of a girl in a two-piece bathing suit, with elaborate skirt draped across her raised arm, 33cm. high. £550

CHINA

GOSS

First Period terracotta
'Keystone of the Kingdome',
life size head of Lord
Beaconsfield, dated 1876.
£400

Dr Samuel Johnson's House,
Lichfield, 75mm. high. £190

Large Carnarvon Ewer with
Welsh Antiquities design of
mistletoe and sickle, crossed
daggers.   £40

Devil looking over Lincoln,
brown, 150mm. high. £100

Model of Hastings Kettle,
55mm. with Barbadoes crest.
£9

Goss Flower Girl Joan,
135mm. high.   £250

Glazed Florence Goss wall vase,
with radiating hair and feathers,
120mm. high.   £250

The Trusty Servant of Win-
chester.   £1,350

Bust of Queen Victoria
wearing mobcap, 130mm.
£125

GRUEBY

Early 20th century Grueby pottery vase, Mass., 4¾in. high. £267

A two-colour Grueby pottery vase, artist's initials A.L. for Annie Lingley, circa 1905, 8¼in. diam. £1,783

Grueby pottery butterscotch glazed vase, artist's initials W.P. for Wilamina Post, dated 3/12/06, 9in. diam. £3,513

A Grueby pottery two-colour vase, elongated bottle neck on spherical cabbage form, circa 1905, 9¼in. high. £2,812

Late 19th century Grueby Faience Co. bust of 'Laughing Boy', based on a statue by Donatello, 11in. high. £972

Grueby pottery vase and Tiffany font, Boston, Massachusetts, circa 1905, with repeating leaves, artist initialled W. F., 10½in. £2,285

Grueby pottery monumental floor vase, Boston, Massachusetts, circa 1905, the body with repeating broad thumb moulded and ribbed decoration, 21in. high. £2,285

A two-colour Grueby pottery vase, Boston, Mass., circa 1905, 8¼in. high. £1,297

A Grueby pottery experimental drip glaze vase, Boston, Massachusetts, circa 1905, with wide rolled rim and short neck, 11¼in. high. £2,285

HAMADA

A stoneware bowl by Shoji Hamada on shallow foot, covered in a dark mushroom coloured glaze, with a grey splash to rim, circa 1955, 11cm. high.   £3,300

A stoneware press-moulded rectangular bottle by Shoji Hamada, brushed with panels of tenmoku and brown glaze, with printed label Made in Japan, circa 1961, 19.8cm. high.   £2,860

A stoneware bowl by Shoji Hamada with circular base and flared sides, covered in a textured green and grey glaze, 23.1cm. diam.   £715

A stoneware waisted cylindrical vase, by Shoji Hamada, the exterior covered in a mirrored black glaze with combed bands through to a khaki glaze, 21.5cm. high.   £2,200

A stoneware cut-sided vase by Shoji Hamada, the square-section body tapering to a circular foot, circa 1960, 20.7cm. high.   £4,400

A stoneware cut-sided waisted cylindrical vase by Shoji Hamada, the exterior covered in a lustrous iron-brown and olive-green mottled glaze, circa 1955, 17.4cm. high.   £3,300

A stoneware press-moulded rectangular bottle by Shoji Hamada with tapering square neck, covered in a speckled olive green glaze, circa 1955, 20cm. high.   £3,080

A stoneware cylindrical jar by Shoji Hamada, gently swollen at the waist, with iron-brown brushwork, 10cm. high. £550

A stoneware press-moulded rectangular bottle by Shoji Hamada with tapering square neck, covered in a speckled olive green glaze, circa 1960. 20.2cm. high.   £3,080

HIRADO

Late 19th century well-modelled Hirado blue and white group of five playful karashishi, 18.8cm. high. £518

Late 19th century Hirado blue and white oviform vase, 26.2cm. high. £756

One of a pair of late 19th century Hirado saucer-shaped dishes, each decorated in Kutani style, 61.2cm. diam. £3,850

IMARI

A pair of late 19th century Imari bijin, 48cm. high. £1,430

A late 19th century Japanese Imari porcelain large charger. £400

One of a pair of late 19th century Imari moulded rectangular sake bottles, 27.5cm. high. £660

ITALIAN

Early 20th century majolica ewer with swan handle, 17½in. high. £256

A 1950's Italian china Galle figure of a kneeling semi-dressed female figure, 18in. high. £500

An Italian ceramic figure designed by E. Mazzolani, of a young girl with bobbed hair, wearing a short dress and leaning against a post, 1929. £990

63

JAPANESE

CHINA

Late 19th century Yabu
Meizan koro and cover with
knop finial, signed, 9cm. diam.
£1,100

A pair of late 19th century
Japanese polychrome bottle
vases, 25in. high.   £1,550

Japanese porcelain wall
plaque, decorated with two
birds on a pine tree, 18½in.
diameter.   £340

KINKOZAN

Late 19th century Kinkozan
oviform vase and cover,
impressed seal mark, signed
Kinkozan zo, 15.5cm. high.
£1,430

A Kinkozan type pottery koro
and cover of globular lobed
quatrefoil shape, signed, 7½in.
high.   £1,595

Late 19th century Kinkozan
baluster vase, signed Dai
Nihon Teikoku Kinkozan zo
Kyoto Awata-yaki Shozan
hitsu, 31cm. high.   £3,300

KYOTO

Late 19th century shaped
and pierced baluster Kyoto
vase decorated in coloured
enamels and gilt, signed
Donzan seizo, 17cm. high.
£1,350

Late 19th century Kyoto
square dish with canted
corners, 15.7cm. sq. £660

Late 19th century Kyoto
vase decorated in coloured
enamels and gilt, signed
Ryozan, 21.5cm. high.
£1,404

LEACH

A rare stoneware bowl decorated by Bernard Leach, with lustrous tenmoku brushwork of Viking Longboats, the rim with pale blue glaze, circa 1955, 30.6cm. diam. £3,750

An early stoneware jug by Bernard Leach, the bulbous body on shallow foot with strap handle and pinched lip, circa 1930, 8.7cm. high. £132

A rare blue and white porcelain plate by Bernard Leach, the shallow well lightly incised with fishermen in boats before mountains, 19.5cm. diam. £1,870

A stoneware flattened rectangular slab bottle by Bernard Leach covered in a dark olive green tea-dust glaze, circa 1965, 18.5cm. high. £748

A rare slip trailed raku bowl by Bernard Leach on shallow foot covered in a pale sand coloured, finely crackled, translucent glaze, circa 1923, 25.2cm. diam. £770

A St. Ives stoneware twin-handled vase, by Bernard Leach, with charcoal coloured brush strokes reserved against a speckled olive glaze, 26cm. high. £420

A tenmoku stoneware pilgrim plate by Bernard Leach with a pilgrim before mountains, impressed BL and St. Ives seals, circa 1970, 32.4cm. diam. £6,050

A tall stoneware press-moulded bottle vase by Bernard Leach with short neck and everted rim, circa 1966, 36.7cm. high. £2,420

A rare stoneware globular vase by Bernard Leach on circular foot and with short neck, covered in a pale celadon glaze with grey veining, circa 1930, 19.8cm. high. £2,860

LENCI

A stylish Lenci pottery figure, modelled as a woman wearing a brown and beige striped dress, 23cm. high. £1,050

A Lenci figure of a rooster, painted marks Lenci 1936 S.P., 29cm. high. £1,080

A Lenci centrepiece modelled as a young naked girl, 46cm. high. £880

LINTHORPE

A Linthorpe pottery ewer, designed by Christopher Dresser, the reddish body glazed on the shoulders with streaked milky-green and brown, 24cm. high. £200

A Linthorpe earthenware vase moulded on each side with grotesque fish faces, 17.9cm. high. £385

A Linthorpe pottery pouring vessel, designed by Christopher Dresser, the domed vessel decorated with vertical beading, 16.5cm. high. £620

A Linthorpe pottery vase, designed by Christopher Dresser, decorated with stylised linear patterns, 21cm. high. £720

A Linthorpe pottery jardiniere designed by Dr Christopher Dresser, the swollen dimpled form with foliate rim, decorated with double loop handles and alternating rosettes, 13.8cm. high. £264

A Linthorpe brown glazed pottery clock case, possibly designed by Christopher Dresser, 10in. high, impressed Linthorpe 1973. £143

CHINA

LJERKA NJERS

A porcelain circular landscape dish, by Ljerka Njers, the un-glazed body textured with muslin, 25.9cm. diam. £183

A porcelain circular landscape dish, by Ljerka Njers, dated 86, 32.7cm. diam. £286

An earthenware charger by Ljerka Njers, inscribed on the reverse L. Njers 1983, 39.4cm. wide. £308

LOUIS WAIN

A Louis Wain porcelain lion vase, decorated in black, yellow, green and russet enamels, 11.8cm. high. £935

A Louis Wain porcelain vase, decorated in blue, green, yellow and russet enamels, with painted marks Louis Wain, Made in England, 14.5cm. high. £352

A Louis Wain porcelain pig vase, decorated in green, yellow, russet and black enamels, with impressed and painted marks, 12.4cm. high. £1,540

MARBLEHEAD

A three-colour Marblehead pottery vase, Massachusetts, circa 1905, the short flared rim on squat bulbous body, initialled by Hannah Tutt, 3½in. high. £457

A Marblehead pottery four-colour vase, signed H.T. for Hannah Tutt, circa 1915, 4½in. high, 4.1/8in. diam. £625

Decorated Marblehead pottery vase, circa 1905, decorated with overall brown latticework on green ground, 6in. high. £1,200

MARTINWARE

A Martin Brothers stoneware vase, 23.5cm. high, signed 'Martin Bros. and dated '8-1903' and 'No. 6'. £160

A Martin Brothers stoneware 'Gourd' vase, 17.5cm. high, signed 'Martin Bros., London & Southall', dated '2-1910. £120

A Martin Bros stoneware two-handled spirit flask, 9½in. high, London and Southall, 1901. £700

An unusual Martin Brothers stoneware toby jug, modelled as the full length seated figure of a bearded man, 25.5cm. high. £3,000

A Martin Brothers jardiniere, incised and painted in blue with mythological figures in a flowering landscape, signed on the rim and base R. W. Martin & Brothers, London and Southall 1886, 31cm.high. £1,980

A rare and highly unusual Martin Brothers stoneware bird, modelled as a likeness of Benjamin Disraeli, 37cm. high. £8,500

A Martinware stoneware gourd vase, the oviform body incised and cross hatched at the neck with green, 9½in. high. £380

A Martin Bros. stoneware tobacco jar and cover, modelled as a grotesque grinning cat, 1885, 22cm. high. £7,560

A Martin Brothers 'Fish' vase, covered in a mottled grey-blue and green glaze and decorated with caricatures of fish, dated 1.1898, 16.1cm. high. £352

MAW

A Maw & Co. circular pottery charger painted in a ruby red lustre with winged mythical beast, 13½in. diam. £209

A Maw & Co. pottery vase, the body painted in a ruby red lustre with large flowers and foliage all on a yellow ground, 13in. high. £352

'The Six Swans', a Maw and Co., two-handled lustre vase designed by Walter Crane, the base with enamelled monogram and dated 1890, 26.7cm. high. £3,850

MEISSEN

A large Meissen group of Count Bruhl's tailor on a goat, blue crossed swords and incised numeral marks, circa 1880, 43cm. high. £2,420

A pair of Meissen condiment groups modelled as a man and a woman, blue crossed swords and incised numeral marks, circa 1880, 20cm. high. £605

A Meissen kinderbuste, blue crossed swords and incised numeral marks, circa 1880, 25cm. high. £550

METTLACH

Mettlach vase, circa 1896, with etched scenes depicting children playing, impressed marks, 15in. high. £229

A Mettlach circular plaque decorated after Stahl, in white relief on a blue grey ground with two sea nymphs, 20½in. £760

A Mettlach two handled stoneware vase, the handles shaped as elephant heads, with incised signature, 34.5cm. high. £220

MINTON

A Minton figural lamp stand, impressed Minton 1517 and with date code for 1881, 35.6cm. high.
£1,836

A Minton majolica-ware teapot and cover in the form of a monkey, 15.5cm. high, impressed Mintons, model no. 1844, date code for 1876.   £620

A large Minton 'moon flask' vase with two lug handles, circa 1890, 43.2cm. high.
£378

A large Minton majolica umbrella stand modelled as a stork, impressed Minton 1916, 102cm. high.   £2,750

A pair of Minton pate-sur-pate two-handled vases of rectangular baluster section in the Oriental style, decorated by T. Mellor, with a bird hovering above flowering plants, circa 1880, 26cm. high.   £550

A Minton pate-sur-pate vase and cover by Marc Louis Solon, 35cm. high, date code for 1903.   £2,000

A Minton majolica garden seat of conical form, the sides pierced with shaped lappets edged with ochre and maroon strapwork, date code for 1883, 45cm. high.   £330

A Minton porcelain dessert plate, the central pate-sur-pate panel signed L. Solon, circa 1880, 9¼in. wide. £300

Minton octagonal garden seat having continuous wide band of Art Nouveau style floral decoration, 17½in. high. £540

MOORCROFT

A 1960's period Moorcroft pottery 'Caribbean' pattern mug, slip trailed and glazed in greens, blues, and reds, with palm trees on sand dunes and yachts at sea, 10cm. high.
£90

A Moorcroft 'Claremont' two-handled vase, circa 1930-1945, decorated in brilliant red and yellow with toadstools on a greenish glazed ground, 20.3cm. high.
£1,760

A Moorcroft 'Hazledene' inkwell, of square section with circular cover painted in the 'Eventide' palette with trees, 6.8cm. high.
£300

A Moorcroft 'Brown Corn-flower' goblet/vase, supported on a spreading circular foot densely decorated with flowers and foliage, 21.5cm. high.
£520

A Moorcroft 'Flambe' pottery plate, painted with a colourful fish and a jellyfish, circa 1935, 25.8cm.
£520

A ginger jar and cover, by Walter Moorcroft, factory mark and potter to the Queen, circa 1945, 11in. high.
£300

A Moorcroft two-handled vase, designed for James MacIntyre & Co., circa 1904-1913, the white ground with trailing flowers in red, blue and green glaze, 23.3cm. high.
£770

An early 20th century tulip pattern Moorcroft 'Florian' ware jardiniere, of cylindrical form with slightly flared and crimped rim, 20cm. high.
£780

A Moorcroft large baluster vase, the white ground piped with mountainous landscape, 37cm. high.
£1,980

CHINA

PARIS

A Paris gilt bronze mounted vase, imitation incised inter-laced L and blue marks, circa 1900, 44cm. high.
£770

A large Paris biscuit group entitled 'Le Nid' after the original sculpture by A. O. Croisy, circa 1880, 38.5cm. high.
£1,430

One of a pair of late 19th century Paris porcelain urns, 10½in. high.
£287

PARIAN

A large Parian group entitled 'Detected', signed R.J. Morris, 41cm. high.
£160

A white bisque bust of Venus modelled with head turned to her left, 17½in. high.
£247

Late 19th century parian figure composition depicting Bacchus and Ariadne embracing, 20in. high.
£200

Maisons bisque porcelain bust of Minerva, Charenton, France, late 19th century, marked base, 34½in. high.
£1,396

A coloured Parian group modelled as a young girl on rockwork, entitled 'You can't read', 12¼in. high, possibly by Robinson & Leadbetter.
£150

A Goss Parian wall vase with head of Georgiana Jewitt, white unglazed, chipped and marked.
£70

72

PILKINGTON

A small Pilkington Royal Lancastrian lustre vase, with a formal pattern of dots, wavy lines, spiral motifs and stylised leaves, 1905, 9cm. high. £110

A Pilkington Royal Lancastrian lustre bowl, the exterior decorated with six rectangular cartouches of stylised foliate design, code for 1910, 19.3cm. diam. £385

Royal Lancastrian lustre pottery vase by W. S. Mycock, dated 1925, 9in. high. £125

A Pilkington Lancastrian baluster vase with everted rim, decorated by Walter Crane, 26.6cm. high. £550

A Pilkington Royal Lancastrian lustre vase decorated by Gordon Forsyth, with a pattern of silvery-yellow stylised cornflowers with their stems against a green ground with red spots, 1910, 23cm. high. £1,100

A large Pilkingtons Lancastrian pottery vase, designed by Gordon Forsyth, painted in a golden lustre of foliage, 17in. high, circa 1919. £500

A Pilkington Lancastrian baluster vase, covered in a blue glaze, decorated in ruby and yellow lustre with stylised flowers, date code for 1908, 19.5cm. high. £308

A lustre Pilkington 'Royal Lancastrian' oviform vase, painted by Richard Joyce, 30.5cm. high. £600

A Pilkington Royal Lancastrian lustre vase, decorated by Richard Joyce, of shouldered, flaring, cylindrical form with everted neck, 24.4cm. high. £500

POOLE POTTERY

CHINA

A Poole pottery earthenware oviform vase, painted by Anne Hatchard, 28cm. high. £242

A pottery table decoration modelled as a yacht in full sail, glazed white, on turquoise base moulded with waves, impressed *Poole,* 15½in. high. £110

A terracotta twin handled oviform vase painted by Ruth Pavely with bluebirds and foliage between contrasting borders, impressed *CSA Ltd.* mark, 6½in. high. £660

REDWARE

A glazed redware grotesque jug, H. F. Rhinhardt, Vale, North Carolina, late 19th/early 20th century, squat form with applied facial features, 7¼in. high. £795

A large Redware bowl or pot, probably Penn., 12in. diam. £617

A redware glazed and decorated wallpocket, American, 1875, with pierced holes for mounting, 10in. high. £168

A manganese decorated Redware jar, by John W. Bell, 1880-95, 12½in. high. £297

A glazed redware cake mould, Pennsylvania, 19th century, with scalloped edge and fluted channels, 9in. diam. £64

A G. E. Ohr moulded pitcher, Biloxi, Mississippi, late 19th century, with Grover Cleveland on one side and his wife on the reverse (some chips), 8in. high. £400

A small stoneware sgraffito bowl by Lucie Rie, covered in a translucent finely crackled mustard-yellow glaze, circa 1955, 6.1cm. high.
£770

A sgraffito inlaid bowl and cover by Lucie Rie, the exterior with radiating inlaid purple lines, circa 1966, 18.2cm. diam. £2,420

A stoneware bowl by Lucie Rie, covered in a pinkish-white pitted and mottled glaze, impressed LR seal, circa 1955, 22.9cm. diam. £1,650

An important large stoneware vase by Lucie Rie, with areas of bluish buff thinning and pooling in places, to reveal body beneath, impressed LR seal, circa 1960, 47cm. high.
£2,860

A large stoneware bowl by Lucie Rie on shallow foot, covered in a rich pitted yellow-uranium glaze, impressed LR seal, 35.6cm. diam. £4,180

A tall stoneware bottle vase, by Lucie Rie, circa 1967, 38.7cm. high. £4,180

An early stoneware vase by Lucie Rie, covered in an olive-green glaze oxidising in places to a lustrous black, 27.1cm. high. £825

A stoneware coffee pot and cover by Lucie Rie, the bulbous body with pulled handle and tall cylindrical neck with pulled lip, impressed LR seal, circa 1966, 22.9cm. high. £440

A stoneware vase by Lucie Rie, covered in a pitted and mottled pale-pink, olive-green and brown glaze, circa 1966, 24cm. high. £3,300

CHINA

ROOKWOOD

A Rookwood pottery deco-
rated creamer, Ohio, 1893,
artist's initials O.G.R. for
Olga Geneva Reed, 4¼in.
high. £106

Rookwood Pottery Flower
vase, Cincinnati, Ohio, 1886,
spherical clay body, impressed
'RP/189/Y' and signed 'M.A.D.'
by Matt Daly, 7½in. diam.
£106

A Rookwood stoneware vase,
the compressed globular body
painted in browns, amber and
green with three wild roses,
21cm. high. £286

A Rookwood pottery jewelled
porcelain vase, signed by
Kataro Shirayamadani, Ohio,
1924, 7in. high. £875

Rookwood pottery tall
portrait vase, Cincinnati,
1894, decorated with figure
entitled 'Spirit of the Sum-
mit', 14½in. high. £2,867

A Rookwood pottery stan-
dard glaze pillow vase, 1889,
artist's initials ARV for
Albert R. Valentien, 14in.
high. £595

A Rookwood pottery standard
glaze portrait vase, decorated
with portrait of a black African
with a cap, 1897, 12in. high.
£1,351

A Rookwood pottery scenic
vellum loving cup, initialled
by Frederick Rothebusch,
1908, 7¼in. high. £625

A Rookwood pottery vase,
decorated by K. Shirayamadani, Roman II for 1902,
38cm. high. £1,430

ROYAL COPENHAGEN

'Faun and Nymph', a Royal Copenhagen group by Gerhard Henning, the crouched figures embracing on a grassy knoll, 28cm. high. £850

Royal Copenhagen poly-chromed porcelain fairytale group, marked June 10, 1955, 8in. high. £590

Royal Copenhagen poly-chromed porcelain fairytale group, Denmark, marked April 25, 1955, 8.5/8in. high. £555

ROYAL DUX

A Royal Dux pottery toilette mirror, depicting an Art Nouveau maiden. £620

An impressive pair of Royal Dux porcelain large figures, the young goatherd standing wearing a brown tunic; and a young shepherdess, wearing a brown blouse and fleece skirt, 67cm. and 64cm. high. £700

A Royal Dux figure of a girl, seated, nude, upon a foliage encrusted rocky base tinted in pink, beige, green, and gilt, 48cm. high. £440

A Royal Dux Art Nouveau conch shell group with three water nymphs in relief, 17½in. high. £470

Royal Dux 'Austria' Art Nouveau vase having fold-over leaf top, 14in. high. £65

A Royal Dux porcelain figure group of a Roman charioteer, the chariot drawn by two rearing horses, 46cm. overall. £780

RUSKIN

A Ruskin high-fired porcelain ginger jar and cover, glazed in sang-de-boeuf shading through mauve to white, 25cm. high, 1925.   £1,800

A Ruskin lustre vase covered with a variegated green/grey glaze exhibiting a silver sheen, 17.1cm. high.   £130

A Ruskin high-fired porcelain vase covered with a rich sang-de-boeuf glaze thinning to white at the neck, 18.5cm. high, impressed 'Ruskin Pottery 1910'.   £700

A Ruskin high fired pottery vase, with everted rim in mottled deep red and white glazes, 8½in. high.   £352

A Ruskin high-fired porcelain ewer, covered overall with a sang-de-boeuf glaze shading to plum with random green speckling, 21cm. high.   £340

A Ruskin high-fired vase of flaring cylindrical form with everted rim, 10in. high. £225

A Ruskin high-fired porcelain vase, glazed in sang-de-boeuf and having random spots of green, 21.8cm. high.   £450

A Ruskin high-fired porcelain bowl glazed in sang-de-boeuf thinning to white, 20cm. diam., and a Ruskin porcelain stand.   £680

A Ruskin high-fired porcelain vase, with a rich sang-de-boeuf glaze shading through mottled areas of plum mauve and grey-green, 23.5cm. high.   £440

CHINA

RUSSIAN

A commemorative porcelain covered cup and saucer, with Russian inscription *'In memory of 200 years of the Founding of St. Petersburg'*, by the Gardner Factory, circa 1903. £330

A large tapering cylindrical porcelain vase, by the Imperial Porcelain Factory (period of Nicholas II), dated 1904, 18½in. high. £2,310

A Soviet porcelain propaganda plate 'The Red Star', with gold borders enclosing a hammer and a plough, by the State Porcelain Factory, circa 1922, 9½in. diam. £12,100

SATSUMA

Late 19th century Satsuma teapot and cover modelled as a stylised bird, 18cm. long. £880

Late 19th century Satsuma moulded oviform jar and cover, depicting the story of Bishamon and Kichigo-ten, 42cm. high. £1,540

Late 19th century Satsuma model of a courtier, signed Dai Nihon, 22.5cm. high. £825

SATURDAY EVENING GIRLS

Saturday Evening Girls pottery motto plate, Mass., circa 1914, signed S.G. for Sara Galner, 7½in. diam. £2,569

Saturday Evening Girls large decorated bowl, Boston, Massachusetts, 1914, with white geese outlined in black, dia. 11½in. £685

Saturday Evening Girls decorated pitcher. Mass., 1911, 9¾in. high. £565

SEVRES

Late 19th century Sevres pattern gilt bronze mounted two-handled centrepiece, 27.5cm. wide.   £605

One of a pair of late 19th century Sevres pattern gilt bronze mounted ewers, 24.5cm. high.   £462

A Sevres circular tazza for the Paris Exhibition of 1878, 36.5cm. high.   £1,045

A Sevres-pattern ormolu-mounted two-handled vase and cover, the turquoise ground reserved and painted with Europa, circa 1875, 57cm. high.   £825

One of a pair of late 19th century Sevres pattern turquoise-ground gilt bronze mounted jardinieres, 27cm. high overall.   £1,320

One of a pair of late 19th century Sevres pattern green-ground vases and covers, 42cm. high.   £1,430

A Sevres-pattern porcelain and ormolu mounted mantel clock, imitation interlaced L and initial marks, circa 1880, 61.5cm. high.   £2,592

A pair of large Sevres-style vases, each painted on one side with a couple in a country landscape, late 19th century, signed Maglin.   £2,200

A Sevres Art Deco porcelain figure of a lady in evening dress designed by Odart-chenko, 28cm. high. £378

SHELLEY

Shelley Bi-plane, No. 344, with fixed propeller, 150mm. long, bearing a transfer of Peterborough. £65

Art Deco 'Shelley' teaset of five cups, six saucers, six side plates, cake plate and bowl, numbered R11792E. £80

A Shelley Intarsio teapot in the form of a caricature of Austin Chamberlain. £320

ST IVES

A St. Ives stoneware jug covered in a translucent inky-blue glaze, 19.2cm. high. £77

An early St. Ives small earthenware jug with strap handle incised St. Ives 1927, 6.5cm. high. £660

A tall St. Ives commemorative stoneware jug with strap handle, 29.1cm. high. £132

STAFFORDSHIRE

A George Jones 'majolica' circular cheese dish and cover, circa 1880, 28cm. diam. £330

A Staffordshire phrenology bust by L. N. Fowler, the cranium printed with divisions named with character interpretations, 19th century, 30cm. high. £585

Late 19th century Staffordshire jug and basin set with floral decoration. £70

STONEWARE

A stoneware oviform jar by Charles Vyse, 1928, 17cm. high. £165

A stoneware asymmetrical sack-shaped vase by Ewen Henderson, 56cm. high. £1,100

A stoneware vase, by John Ward, impressed JW seal, circa 1984, 22.4cm. high. £220

A stoneware dish by Kitaoji Rosanjin, partly covered in a pale olive-green glaze, 19.1cm. diam. £880

A stoneware jug by Janice Tchalenko, with pulled lip and strap handle, 24cm. high. £132

A stoneware platter by Raymond Finch, decorated by Henry Bergen, Winch-combe Pottery seals, 39cm. diam. £660

A decorated stoneware vase, attributed to Russell G. Crook, 1906-12, 9½in. high. £446

A stoneware dish by Ewen Henderson, with irregular rim, 35cm. wide. £330

A narrow waved stoneware vase by Joanna Constantinidis, with sagged rim, 1984, 46.3cm. high. £385

CHINA

TECO

A Teco pottery moulded lotus flower vase, Chicago, circa 1905, designed by F. Moreau, 11½in. high. £1,621

Teco pottery matt green vase, Illinois, circa 1908, with four open handles, 6½in. high. £485

A Teco Art pottery fluted vase, Illinois, circa 1905, 10½in. high. £750

VAN BRIGGLE

One of two 20th century Van Briggle pottery vases, Colorado, one 2¾in. high, the other 5½in. high. £225

A Rookwood pottery basket, by artist Artus Van Briggle, decorated in slip underglaze with blossoms, berries and leaves, 6½in. high. £414

Van Briggle pottery copper clad vase, Colorado, 5½in. high. £839

VIENNA

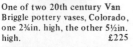

Late 19th century 'Vienna' rectangular porcelain plaque, painted with three vestal virgins, 32 x 26cm. £770

A 'Vienna' circular dish, the centre painted with the Three Graces, imitation blue beehive mark, circa 1900, 35.5cm. diam. £660

A 'Vienna' rectangular plaque painted by C. Meinelt after Murillo, signed and impressed blue enamelled beehive mark, circa 1880, 44 x 35cm. £9,900

WEDGWOOD

A Wedgwood Fairyland lustre black-ground small globular jar and cover, circa 1925, 8.5cm. high. £1,430

John Skeaping Wedgwood figure of a kangaroo seated on a rectangular base, 8½in. high, circa 1930. £300

A Wedgwood Masonic handled jug, white ground, cobalt-blue neck and gilded rim, circa 1935, 7in. high. £40

Late 19th century Wedgwood blue ground jasper jardiniere, 10in. diam. £135

A pair of Wedgwood flame fairyland lustre tapering oviform vases, designed by Daisy Makeig-Jones, decorated with pixies, elves and bats crossing bridges, 1920s, 29.5cm. high. £3,960

A Wedgwood ceramic ewer and basin designed by George Logan, covered in a lilac glaze and decorated with stylised yellow floral designs, 29.6cm. height of ewer. £770

A Wedgwood bone china powder-blue ground massive yan-yan vase, outlined in gilt and painted in natural colours with a polar bear and cub, circa 1920, 56.5cm. high. £1,210

Very rare Wedgwood 'Woodland Elves' fairyland lustre bowl signed by Daisy Makeig-Jones, 8¾in. diam., circa 1923. £4,285

Wedgwood bust in moonstone glaze, of Princess Elizabeth, the present Queen, modelled as a young girl in 1937, 15in. high. £460

WEIMAR

A Weimar ceramic earthenware cake plate, 31cm. diam., together with another 28cm. diam. £100

A Weimar ceramic porcelain oviform chocolate jug, 19cm. high, printed factory mark Leuchtenburg. £50

A Weimar ceramic earthenware cake plate, 22.8cm. diam., together with eight others, various. £150

WELLER

Louwelsa Weller pottery Indian portrait vase, Ohio, circa 1915, 10¾in. high. £296

Pair of Weller 'Ivory Ware' jardinieres on stands, Zanesville, Ohio, circa 1915, 35in. high, 18in. diam. £1,657

A Weller Sicard twisted pottery vase, iridescent purples and greens with snails in the design, circa 1907, unsigned, 7½in. high. £324

WEMYSS

A Wemyss ware pottery fruit basket, the body painted with cockerels and hens in brown, black, pink and green enamels, 30cm. wide. £820

A Wemyss preserve pot and lid painted with oranges and foliage, green painted mark, 4in. high. £70

A large Wemyss pig, the seated animal painted with pink leafy roses, 43.5cm. from snout to tail. £3,080

WORCESTER

A Royal Worcester porcelain jug (ice tusk), circa 1884, approx. 12in. tall. £310

Royal Worcester 'Sabrina' porcelain circular dished plate, signed R. Austin, 1929, 9.5in. diam. £40

A Royal Worcester pierced oviform two-handled vase, painted by H. Chair, with swags of roses suspended from a band of pierced ornament, date code for 1909, 16cm. high. £880

A pair of Royal Worcester polychrome figures of semi-naked women, representing 'Joy' and 'Sorrow', 25.5cm., circa 1885. £250

A Royal Worcester 'Aesthetic' teapot and cover, one side modelled as a youth wearing mauve cap, the reverse as a girl in mauve bonnet, 1882, 15cm. high. £1,320

A pair of Royal Worcester lobed vases potted in the Persian manner, with pierced rims and foliage handles, 49.5cm., 1885. £700

Royal Worcester flower bowl, shape no. 1713, green circle and crown mark, date code 1900, 9in. high. £420

One of a pair of ovoid ewer-shaped vases, signed A. Shuck, 24cm. high, shape no. 1944, date codes for 1912. £1,250

A Royal Worcester two-handled, footed bulbous vase, by Harry Davis, model no. 1428, puce mark, 1932, 12in. high. £5,250

ZSOLNAY

A small Zsolnay lustre vase decorated with scrollwork and stylised foliage in golden-green lustre, 10cm. high. £130

Late 19th century Zsolnay Pecs pottery vase in the form of a Pre-Columbian vessel, 34cm. long. £165

A Zsolnay pottery lustre ewer decorated with sinuous silver-grey stems and ruby florets against a starred ground, 22.5cm. high. £820

A Zsolnay lustre vase of tapering oviform with narrow neck supported on three sinuous stems rising from a ring base, 23.5cm. high. £480

A large Zsolnay lustre group, of two men possibly Cain and Abel, one lying prostrate on a domed rocky base with the other towering above him, 37.5cm. high. £550

A Zsolnay oviform lustre vase painted in vivid reds, yellows and greens with exotic flowers and foliage, 26.5cm. high. £750

A Zsolnay ceramic jug, the handle formed as an Art Nouveau maiden with flowing hair and dress, 22.8cm. high. £220

A Zsolnay Pecs lustre group, modelled as two polar bears on a large rock in a green and blue golden lustre, 4½in. high. £250

A small Zsolnay figural lustre vase decorated on the shoulders with the partially clad Orpheus with his lyre beside him and an amorous mermaid, 13cm. high. £680

BRACKET CLOCKS

An Edwardian mahogany bracket clock, the 19cm arched gilt brass dial with black Roman numerals and Arabic seconds, stylised paw feet, 73cm high. £1,000

A 19th century rosewood and inlaid quarter chiming bracket clock, the arched case inlaid with an urn, the three train movement with anchor escapement, 1ft.8in. high. £650

A Victorian mahogany eight-day chiming and striking bracket clock with 7¼in. arched brass dial, 23¼in. high. £800

Late 19th century mahogany 8-day domed bracket clock with silvered dial, 12in. high. £240

A late 19th century three-train musical bracket clock, in the 18th century manner, inscribed Henry Ruttiman Lucerne, 50cm. £1,100

A late Victorian burr walnut chiming bracket clock, the arched engraved silvered dial signed Thwaites & Reed London, 22½in. £825

A substantial Edwardian bracket clock with arched brass dial, fronting a three-train movement with Westminster chime. £960

A hammered copper shelf clock, by Tiffany & Co., New York, early 20th century, on rectangular brass platform base, 11in. high. £628

A late 19th century bracket clock in ebonised case with gilt metal mounts, full chimes of Westminster and Eight Bells, 34in. high overall, by Canova, Halesworth and Southwold. £2,300

CARRIAGE CLOCKS

A silver-cased minute-repeating carriage clock, inscribed E. White, London, with lever platform escapement striking the quarters on two gongs, 3½in. high. £3,080

A Swiss miniature silver and enamel carriage timepiece, the lever movement with circular enamel dial, 5cm. high, signed for Asprey. £340

A silver gilt carriage timepiece, the case with coloured stone corner decorations, the lever movement with circular enamel dial, 4in. high. £500

A silver and enamel carriage timepiece, decorated in blue enamel with circular enamel dial, signed for H.Gibbs, London, 4½in. high. £360

An unusual miniature carriage timepiece, late 19th century, the movement with platform lever escapement, signed Bigelow, Kennard & Co., Boston. £924

A 19th century Continental silver miniature carriage timepiece, the lever movement with enamel dial, 4in. high, marked London 1895. £400

A 19th century French brass carriage clock, 7in. high, together with a leather travelling case. £500

An unusual gilt brass carriage timepiece, the fusee movement signed Viner on the backplate, rectangular case with turned corner columns, 5¼in. high. £660

A 19th century French gilt brass carriage clock, the lever movement striking on a gong with push repeat, 19cm. high. £550

CLOCK SETS

A 19th century French silver plated three-piece clock garniture, the striking movement by S. Marti & Cie, 16in. high, together with two five-light candelabra, 19in. high. £450

A Sevres pattern pink-ground porcelain and gilt bronze composite garniture-du-cheminee, circa 1880, the clock 34cm. wide, the vases 26.5cm. high. £810

An ormolu and bronze garniture de cheminee of Louis XV style, with a group of three putti playing musical instruments, second half 19th century. £1,760

Late 19th century gilt metal clock set of Renaissance style, the clock 28in. high, the candelabra 39½in. high. £2,200

A clock garniture in the Louis XVI style, signed in the centre 'Goldsmiths' Alliance Ltd./Cornhill, London', 12½in. high. £400

A French veined marble garniture, 17in. high. £418

CLOCK SETS

1930's black and brown marble clock set in the Art Deco style. £100

A French ormolu and porcelain mounted three-piece clock garniture, the clock 13in. high, the side pieces 13¾in. high. £475

A French white marble and gilt metal mounted composite clock garniture, the mantel clock on column supports with drum shaped case surmounted by an urn finial and a pair of twin-branch candelabra, 11in. high. £418

A good ormolu and porcelain garniture, 18in. high. £1,540

A white marble and gilt metal three-piece clock set, by J. Marti & Cie., the clock 23in. high, the urns 17in. high. £950

A 19th century French gilt and patinated bronze three piece clock garniture, of small proportions, the movement stamped 'H & F Paris'; the gilded case in the form of a staved barrel lying on its side draped with a fruiting vine and flanked by two scantily clad, animated, patinated bronze putti, 19cm. high. £520

LONGCASE CLOCKS

A mahogany longcase clock, the brass dial inscribed Maple & Co. Ltd., London, 7ft. 11in. high.   £680

Westminster chime grandmother clock, no pendulum, 1920.   £150

An Edwardian painted satinwood longcase clock, the chapter ring signed Wm. Fastwood, 8ft.2in. high.   £1,944

A mahogany cased three-weight Westminster chime grandfather clock, circa 1900. £600

An Arts & Crafts oak tallcase clock, by the Colonial Mfg. Co., Zeeland, Michigan, circa 1914, 84in. high.   £1,081

A late 19th century mahogany longcase clock, in the 18th century style, surmounted by carved and pierced swan neck pediment, inscribed William Alexander & Son, Glasgow, 230cm.   £2,400

An L. & J. G. Stickley tall case clock, signed with red handcraft decal, circa 1908, 81in. high.   £8,928

Late 19th century mahogany quarter chiming longcase clock, signed Maple & Co., London, 2.54m. high. £2,500

LONGCASE CLOCKS

Art Nouveau mahogany tall case clock, late 19th century by Gerr Suss, Hamburg, 96½in. high. **£930**

A carved longcase clock in the form of a woman standing with arms akimbo, signed Joh Ylie Konnig Tlmola, late 19th century, 7ft. high. **£4,620**

An Art Nouveau oak longcase clock, by J. Gruber, 253cm. high. **£2,150**

An Edwardian mahogany longcase clock of small proportions, signed Ollivant and Botsford. **£1,300**

A Gustav Stickley oak tall case clock, circa 1902-04, 71in. high. **£5,381**

A large Regina oak longcase 15½in. disc musical box clock, with eighty-six discs, 252cm. high, circa 1900. **£3,600**

An Austrian beech-wood longcase clock painted to simulate mahogany, circa 1900, 207.9cm. high. **£540**

An early 20th century musical longcase clock, bearing the date 1925, the three-train movement with deadbeat escapement. **£1,600**

93

MANTEL CLOCKS

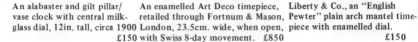

An alabaster and gilt pillar/ vase clock with central milk-glass dial, 12in. tall, circa 1900 £150

An enamelled Art Deco timepiece, retailed through Fortnum & Mason, London, 23.5cm. wide, when open, with Swiss 8-day movement. £850

Liberty & Co., an "English Pewter" plain arch mantel time-piece with enamelled dial.
£150

An Arts & Crafts mahogany mantel clock with bevelled glass, circa 1900, 12in. high. £297

An Arts & Crafts square oak mantel clock, by Seth Thomas Clock Co., 20th century, 12½in. high, 10½in. wide. £648

A Gustav Stickley oak mantel clock, early 20th century, the door with faceted cut-out framing brass dial, Seth Thomas movement, 13¾in. high. £1,714

Late 19th century gilt and patinated bronze and marble industrial clock, probably French, 14½in. high. £1,151

Late 19th century lacquered brass and painted metal lighthouse clock, probably French, 22in. high. £1,535

A Black Forest 'cuckoo' mantel clock, the two train fusee movement with anchor escapement and skeletonised back plate. £308

MANTEL CLOCKS

A Napoleon III brass and champleve lighthouse clock, late 19th century, with spring wound mechanism, on a green onyx base, 20in. high. £2,662

A miniature silver and enamel timepiece, the rectangular case decorated with blue guilloche enamel, the dial signed for Harrods Ltd, 1½in. high. £380

Late 19th century enamelled silver gilt Renaissance style table clock, the case by H. Bohm, Vienna, 7½in. high. £806

A 19th century French gilt brass and champleve enamel four glass mantel clock, 25cm. high. £480

A Lalique square-shaped clock, Inseparables, the clear and opalescent glass decorated with budgerigars, 11cm. high. £1,100

A guilloche enamel desk clock, the split seed-pearl bezel enclosing a white enamel dial with black Arabic chapters, white metal, marked Faberge, 1899-1908, 5in. high. £14,300

Late 19th century Sevres pattern pink-ground porcelain gilt bronze mounted mantel clock, 34cm. high. £770

An electroplated pewter presentation clockcase, surmounted by an Art Nouveau maiden standing contraposto, her arms raised against an elaborate pierced trellis superstructure, 50cm. high. £770

A modern Swiss singing bird box in engine-turned lacquered brass case, surmounted by a French 8-day alarm clock, 6in. high, with travelling case. £1,320

MANTEL CLOCKS

A late 19th century gilt metal French mantel clock in the Louis XIV manner, with celeste bleu porcelain panels, 37cm. £160

An unusual Jaeger LeCoultre table clock in Art Deco style, the straight line eight day movement jewelled to the centre with monometallic balance, 7½in. diam. £242

An Odd Fellows carved box with clock, America, early 20th century, shaped upper section crested with carved eagle, 13½in. high. £227

Victorian rouge marble mantel clock with eight-day French movement and brass dial. £175

A fine hardstone and enamelled silver desk clock, signed Cartier, on agate base, 63mm. high. £3,391

A silvered bronze Art Deco table clock, signed R. Terras, 34.5cm. high. £990

A chromium plated Smiths electric mystery clock, inscribed Smith Electric, with dagger hands, 8in. high. £286

A Sevres pattern gilt bronze mantel clock, the movement by Gasnier a Paris, circa 1875, 41cm. wide. £825

Late 19th century ebonised mantel clock in the Arts and Crafts style with porcelain face and eight day movement. £150

MANTEL CLOCKS

An Ato Art Deco table clock with a pair of bronze owls perched on top, 41.5cm. high. **£495**

A Lalique clock, the satin-finished glass moulded with two pairs of love-birds in blossoming branches, with brown stained decoration, 21.8cm. wide. **£880**

A late 19th century gilt metal French mantel clock in the Louis XV manner, inset with pink porcelain panels, 46cm. **£280**

A Liberty and Co. hammered pewter clock, the body decorated with stylised tree and foliate panels, the copper clock face with black enamel Roman chapters and turquoise enamel centre, 18.2cm. high. **£660**

A rare mixed metal mantel clock by Tiffany & Company, New York, 1880-1885, the front with mokume panels of silver mixed with niello, brass and red metal, 9in. high. **£11,046**

An early electric Eureka table clock in glazed mahogany case, the signed white enamel dial with Roman numerals and subsidiary seconds, dated 1906, 13¼in. high. **£715**

A late 19th century brass cased mantel clock in the French taste, striking the hours and half hours on a coiled gong, 28cm. **£230**

A Jaeger-Le Coultre eight day mantel clock, with Roman chapters, the transparent glass discus-shaped body with chrome rim and foot, 23.3cm. diam. **£528**

A Meissen porcelain clockcase, the circular gilt metal dial with blue Roman numerals, blue crossed swords and incised numeral marks, circa 1880, 60cm. high. **£3,300**

MANTEL CLOCKS

A Galle carved and acid-etched clock, 13cm. high.
£2,860

Kneeling girl with clock, a bronze and ivory figure cast after a model by F. Preiss, 54.4cm. high.   £8,580

Late 19th century red and black marble mantel clock with strike.
£60

A 19th century French porcelain mantel clock, the shaped case applied with flowers, the circular enamel dial signed Hry Marc, a Paris, 1ft 1½in. high.   £640

A French porcelain panelled mantel clock, the movement with Brocot suspension, the dial decorated in the Japanese manner with herons, butterflies and other birds, 13in.
£682

A 19th century French ormolu and porcelain mounted mantel clock, 41cm. high.   £520

An Alfred Dunhill Art Deco marble mantel clock and cigarette case, 23.7cm. high.
£605

A Meissen clockcase with a seated figure of Cupid, blue crossed swords and incised numeral marks, circa 1880, 30cm. high.   £748

A boulle mantel clock in the Louis XV taste, in waisted tortoiseshell and brass inlaid case, 42cm.   £500

MANTEL CLOCKS

A 19th century French gilt brass mantel clock with blue porcelain panels, signed Miller & Sons, London. £680

An ormolu, white marble and soft-paste porcelain mantel clock with circular glazed enamel dial in a waisted basket of flowers and foliage, late 19th century, 11¼in. high. £825

A Meissen clockcase of shaped outline, the movement with circular dial, blue crossed swords mark, circa 1880, 31cm. high. £1,540

A 19th century French porcelain mantel clock, the circular enamel dial signed Hry Marc a Paris, on a shaped base bearing the mark of Jacob Petit, 12in. high. £360

A late 19th century walnut mantel clock, the dial signed Chas. Frodsham, Clock-maker to the Queen, No. 2057, 30cm. high. £750

A late 19th century mantel clock, with back plate signed 'J.W.Benson, London', surmounted by a bronze group of a young man and woman holding a tambourine, 22¼in. high. £600

A 19th century French gilt brass and white marble mantel timepiece, the rectangular case surmounted by a rooster, 7½in. high. £450

A silvered bronze mantel clock, by Edgar Brandt, 30.6cm. high. £3,080

A 19th century ormolu and porcelain mounted mantel clock, the rectangular case surmounted by a figure of a boy riding a dolphin, 12in. high. £620

WALL CLOCKS

An Edwardian mahogany wall clock, inscribed Evans & Sons, Birmingham, over panelled pendulum cover, 162cm. £550

Late 19th century softwood German wall clock, the white enamel dial with 8-day movement, 13in. high.   £420

Late 19th century walnut regulator timepiece, by the Chelsea Clock Co., Mass., 35in. high.   £590

Late 19th century walnut regulator timepiece, by The E. Howard Watch & Clock Co., Boston, 40in. high.   £625

A mahogany wall timepiece, the repainted white enamel convex dial with Roman numerals, moon hands and signed Middleton, London.

£352

A cherry wall regulator timepiece, by Seth Thomas Clock Co., Conn., circa 1880, 36in. long.   £419

A good mahogany striking drop-dial wall clock, with hexagonal bezel, the white painted dial indistinctly signed, 29½in. high. £550

A French electrical wall regulator signed Systeme Campiche de Metz and Mees Nancy on the dial.   £864

A mahogany wall timepiece, the chain fusee movement with anchor escapement, mottled plates signed Dent, London.   £297

WATCHES

A Swiss gold openface watch, signed with Patent No. 98234, the 18ct. gold case, London, 1925, 51mm. diam. £571

An 18ct. gold keyless lever chronograph, the movement with compensated balance, signed J. W. Benson, London, the case marked London 1882, 53mm. diam. £600

An 18ct. gold minute repeating keyless lever watch, the movement signed James Murray, London, 1882, 51mm. diam. £950

An unusual cigarette lighter mounted with a watch, signed 'The Golden Wheel Lighter', fitted with adjusted 6-jewel lever movement, signed Cyma, 52mm. high. £234

An enamelled gold openface dress watch of Napoleonic interest, signed Movado, the 18ct. gold case with London import mark 1910, 47mm. diam. £1,882

An 18ct. gold combined watch and lighter by Dunhill, engine-turned silvered Deco dial with Arabic numerals set in a hinged reeded octagonal frame, 1930, 49mm. high. £2,420

A Continental silver verge watch, the enamel dial mounted with the seated figure of an automated cobbler hammering, 51mm. diam. £260

A fine gold openface centre seconds world time dress watch, retailed by Cartier, the movement by Agassiz. £4,315

An 18ct. gold keyless lever Karrusel watch, the movement signed Charles Fox, Bournemouth, the case marked Chester 1895, 55mm. diam. £2,200

WRISTWATCHES

A gent's Swiss gold Oyster perpetual wristwatch, by Rolex, the signed gilt dial with baton numerals, 29mm. diam.   £550

A circular steel gent's wristwatch, by Pierce, the silvered dial with centre seconds, date, and Arabic numerals, 32mm. diam.   £160

A gent's circular steel automatic wristwatch, by Blancpain, with perpetual calendar, the white dial with subsidiaries for day, date and month, 34mm. diam.
£2,200

A stainless steel Breitling Navitimer in circular case with milled bezel and adjustable calculator scale, with expanding steel bracelet, 40mm. diam.
£308

A gold Audemars Piguet perpetual calendar automatic wristwatch, the signed movement with 36 jewels adjusted to heat, cold, isochronism and five positions, diam. 35mm.
£8,250

A 19ct. gold chronograph wristwatch in circular case, the matt silvered dial signed Universal, Geneve, 33mm. diam.   £605

An 18ct. gold circular gent's wristwatch, by J.W.Benson, the enamel dial with Roman numerals, the case marked London 1916, 34mm. diam.
£420

A Swiss gold cushion shaped gent's wristwatch, by Rolex, with Arabic numerals and subsidiary seconds, 36mm. long.   £250

A fine gold calendar wrist chronograph with perpetual calendar, signed Patek Philippe, Geneve, No. 869392, the nickel 23-jewel movement with monometallic balance.   £23,428

WRISTWATCHES

A gent's Swiss gold Oyster perpetual day-date wristwatch, by Rolex, the signed chocolate coloured dial with centre seconds. £2,600

A Swiss gold circular gent's wristwatch, by Patek Philippe & Co, Geneve, the signed gilt dial marked Gobbi Milano, 32mm. diam. £1,700

A steel Oyster perpetual bubble back gent's wristwatch, by Rolex, Arabic numerals, 39mm. long. £340

An 18ct. gold automatic wristwatch in oval case, the white enamel dial signed Baume & Mercier, Geneve, with very slim automatic movement. £770

A square white gold diamond and baguette sapphire set wristwatch signed on the silvered dial Cartier, Paris, 23mm. square. £5,060

An 18ct gold wristwatch in circular case, the black dial signed Van Cleef & Arpels, the movement signed Piaget, 33mm. £550

A Swiss gold circular gent's wristwatch, by Movado, the signed silvered dial with subsidiary seconds, 36mm. diam. £280

An 18ct. gold Rolex chronograph wristwatch with black bezel, calibrated in units per hour, the silvered dial with applied gold luminous baton numerals, 37mm. diameter. £4,180

A stainless steel calendar and moon phase wristwatch, inscribed 'Universal, Geneve', the signed movement jewelled to the third, diam. 34mm. £275

CLOISONNE

A Namikawa compressed globular tripod censer and domed cover, circa 1900, 10.3cm. diam.   £2,200

Pair of Japanese cloisonne enamel on copper vases, late 19th century, decorated with spring blossoms under a flowering tree, 12in. high.
£457

One of a pair of Chinese cloisonne vases in late Ming style of ovoid form, with waisted necks and splayed cylindrical feet, late 19th century, 15½in. high.
£1,400

Massive Chinese cloisonne enamel Ding-form temple vase, bearing Qianlong reign mark, probably 19th century, 29in. wide.   £2,171

A Chinese 24in. circular cloisonne enamel plaque with chrysanthemum and crane decoration.   £335

Good quality Japanese cloisonne vase, yellow ground with finely worked figure of a bird of paradise and foliage, 5in. high.   £180

A Hattori moriage slender trumpet vase with widely flared foliate rim with metal edging, impressed Hattori seal to the base, late 19th century, 19cm. high.   £1,100

A pair of Japanese cloisonne enamelled vases decorated with cranes among water-lilies, 12in. high.   £600

Cloisonne vase decorated with dragons on a dark-blue field, converted to a reading lamp, 19in. high.   £100

A Japanese cloisonne enamel vase, late 19th century, enamelled with a continuous scene of finely detailed brown sparrows and water-fowl, 18in. high. £1,775

One of a pair of Japanese cloisonne vases, each painted with panels of cockerels and hens and birds in flight, 6¼in. high. £400

Late 19th century cloisonne enamel globular jar and shallow domed cover, 59.5cm. high. £4,180

A Japanese cloisonne enamelled wine pot and cover, the shoulders decorated with a dragon and a Ho-o bird, 5½in. high. £190

Late 19th century Japanese cloisonne urn of baluster form, 19¼in. high. £1,364

A Chinese cloisonne incense burner, the body of tapering rectangular form, standing on four fish like legs, early 20th century, 12in. high. £240

A tall cloisonne vase decorated in various coloured enamels on a dark blue ground with a spray of tiger lilies, late 19th century, 33cm. high. £550

A pair of Japanese cloisonne vases of semi ovoid form decorated with sprays of chrysanthemum, peony, wisteria and lilies, 16in. high. £1,350

A Japanese cloisonne vase of slender baluster form decorated with a dragonfly resting on an iris, 12in. high. £300

Gustav Stickley hammered copper chamberstick circa 1907, with removable flared bobeche and strapwork handle, 9in. high. £228

An Arts and Crafts white metal and copper jewellery casket designed by E. Creswick, with curved hinged cover, set with two cabochon chrysoprases, 1902, 28.8cm. long. £1,320

A Roycroft copper and brass wash handled basket, East Aurora, N.Y., circa 1920, 9in. diam. £54

A hammered copper wine pitcher, no. 80, by the Stickley Bros., circa 1905, 15in. high. £81

Pair of relief decorated copper plaques, signed by Raymond Averill Porter, 1912 and 1913, 10½ x 9½in. £324

A hammered brass umbrella stand, possibly Belgium circa 1900-20, 24in. high. £351

A late Victorian brass coal box with domed lid and pierced finial, 17in. wide. £330

A fine pair of 20th century brass candlesticks, 8½in. high. £202

An Onondaga Metal Shop hammered copper and repousse wall plaque, circa 1905, 20in. diam. £2,972

A Karl Kipp copper vase, model no. 218, East Aurora, N.Y., circa 1919, 6½in. high. £148

A brass pen tray in the form of a roaring hippopotamus with hinged back, 12½in. wide. £3,520

A Hagenauer brass bowl, supported on a broad cylindrical stem pierced with golfing figures, 11cm. high. £360

A Hagenauer brass twin branch candelabrum of interlaced form, the cylindrical sconces with gadrooned oval drip pans, decorated with a stylised dog, 35.5cm. high. £308

Benedict Art Studios hammered copper wall plaque, N.Y., circa 1907, 15in. diam. £560

A Hagenauer brass figure of a tennis player, the stylised male figure in serving position, stamped marks Hagenauer, Wien, wHw, Made in Austria, 27.5cm. high. £770

An oval brass planter with gadroon embossed decoration, 13in. high. £190

Late 19th century Art Nouveau style brass coal box. £61

A Morris & Co. whistling copper and brass kettle, the asymmetrical conical vessel with cylindrical spout and cover, 24cm. high. £170

COPPER & BRASS

Victorian pressed brass magazine rack, 1880. £24

A good large Newlyn copper rosebowl decorated with fish, 9in. diam. £100

A set of brass measures from West Riding County Council, dated 1880, contained in a fitted mahogany case. £760

An Arts & Crafts hammered copper fireplace hood, circa 1910, 43in. high, 12½in. wide at top, 36in. wide at bottom. £486

A pair of brass figures of cavaliers, one holding a mallet, the other a scroll, with inscribed plaques, 19in. high overall. £176

A Benham & Froud brass kettle designed by Dr. C. Dresser, on three spiked feet, 24.5cm. high. £324

A late 19th century ship's brass plaque, enamelled with H.M.S. Centurion Comm[n] 1895-98, 14in. diam. £154

An Edwardian satin brass coal receiver on claw feet. £55

An enamelled hammered copper humidor, by R. Cauman, Boston, circa 1925, 6½in. high. £252

COPPER & BRASS

Victorian brass and oak
letter rack, 1880.   £50

An Arthur Stone decorated
copper bowl, Mass., circa
1910, stamped with Stone
logo, 5¼in. diam.   £3,000

Early 19th century copper
coal helmet, also a matching
shovel, 17½in. high.   £390

A copper and brass diver's
helmet, date 8.29.41, with
clamp screws, valves, plate
glass windows and guards,
20in. high.   £1,210

A Victorian brass and wood
paper rack, circa 1880.   £18

Early 20th century brass fire-
screen with stylised flame
decoration.   £45

A Jean Dunand lacquered
metal bowl, signed in red
lacquer, circa 1925, 10cm.
high.   £864

A French Art Deco circular
copper wall plaque by Claudius
Linossier, with hammered and
silvered surface inlaid with geometric motifs, 50cm. diam.,
signed.   £500

Copper milk churn with
cover.   £66

A dress of ivory silk velvet, the straps embroidered with diamante beadwork, 1920's. £99

A fine marriage coat of white goatskin, stamped with leaves and flowers, 1887. £605

A wedding dress of ivory spotted silk, the blouse pouched above the waist, 1909. £121

A dress of black georgette, the skirt with looped floating panel, labelled Doeuillet, circa 1922. £440

A navy silk dress printed with red, yellow and white circles, labelled Paquin, Paris and London, 1940's. £143

A dress of royal blue silk, with ribbons of ivory silk printed with black chine leaves, circa 1875. £1,155

An evening dress of black chiffon and georgette, the skirt worked with floating panels, labelled Chanel, circa 1928. £1,540

A stunning dress of peach coloured velvet, densely worked with silver, white and peach coloured beads, 1920's. £143

A black velvet evening
dress with narrow
velvet straps, labelled
Chanel, circa 1934.
£660

A turn of the century
black satin pleated
tea gown, the pagoda
sleeves and neck with
tambour lace trim.
£140

A dress of blue muslin,
with a V-neck, em-
broidered all over with
white beads, 1920's.
£132

A late 19th century
pink and blue brocade
silk dress designed
with swags and plumes,
circa 1890's. £200

A sleeveless wrapover
shift of peach velvet,
labelled Becker Fils,
1930's. £176

A suit of pink and
fawn wool, with
metallic thread wefts,
unlabelled, Chanel,
1950's. £143

A summer suit of
white cotton, with a
high collar decorated
with broderie anglaise,
circa 1905. £77

A blue crepe bias cut
evening dress, the
bodice worked as a
jacket, labelled
Schiaparelli, 1937.
£990

DOLLS

A bisque headed doll with open mouth, blonde hair and sleeping eyes, stamped '21, Germany, R6/OP', 14in. £70

A painted felt doll, the felt body jointed at shoulders and hips, dressed in purple silk gown trimmed with organdie and felt, 15in. high, marked Lenci. £220

A 20th century bisque headed doll with brown hair and jointed limbs, 22in. £100

A bisque headed child doll with blue sleeping eyes, blonde wig and jointed body, 23in. high, probably Alt Beck & Gosschalk. £605

A bisque figure of a seated boy, wearing a cream and orange bathing cap, 11½in. high, impressed with the Gebruder Heubach Sunburst and 4859. £660

A shoulder composition doll, with closed mouth, fixed blue glass eyes, fair wig, dressed as a parlour maid. £110

A bisque swivel headed doll, with fixed blue eyes, pierced ears, blonde wig and cloth body, 15½in. high. £440

Kammer and Reinhardt/Simon and Halbig bisque headed character doll, with brown glass sleeping eyes, moulded closed mouth, 21¼in. high. £2,800

A poured wax child doll with fixed blue eyes, the long blonde hair inset in groups into head, 21½in. high, with Lucy Peck oval stamp on body. £440

112

DOLLS

A bisque headed doll with blue sleeping eyes, blonde wig and jointed body, 17in. high, marked '390 A ½ M', in original box stamped 'Toyland, Hull'. £330

A composition mask faced googlie eyed doll, with smiling watermelon mouth, 13in. high, Hug Me Kiddies, circa 1914. £264

'Dancing Sailor', a printed and painted tinplate sailor, in blue cloth uniform, 7½in. high, by Lehmann, circa 1912. £110

A bisque swivel headed bebe with closed mouth, brown paperweight eyes, moulded feathered brows, pierced ears, 18½in. high, marked BRU Jne 6 (one finger damaged). £9,900

A good Lenci cloth doll, Italian circa 1930, the stiffened felt head with painted features, eyes looking to the right and blonde short curly mohair wig, 56cm. high. £520

A long-faced bisque headed bebe with closed mouth, pierced and applied ears, blue paperweight eyes, 19½in. high, head impressed 9, body marked with blue Jumeau Medaille d'Or stamp. £8,250

A bisque headed character child doll with closed pouting mouth, painted blue eyes and blonde mohair wig, marked K*R. £715

A bisque headed doll with open mouth, sleeping eyes and brown hair, stamped with a monogram 'GW', Germany, 16in. £195

A flesh tinted china shoulder head with dark brown mohair wig, 19in. high. £1,870

DOLLS

A Lenci pressed felt girl doll, circa 1930, with moulded and painted facial features and blonde wig, 49cm. high. £220

A Chad Valley painted felt portrait doll modelled as the Princess Elizabeth, circa 1938, 18in. high, together with another and a koala bear. £308

A bisque headed child doll, with brown lashed sleeping eyes, pierced ears and jointed body, 12½in. high, marked S&H. £550

A wooden character doll with carved and painted features, in pink velvet and organza dress and original underwear, 14½in. high, by Schoenhut. £418

A set of Madame Alexander Dionne Quins, the composition dolls with painted facial features, 7in. high. £374

A Kathe Kruse fabric boy doll with short wig, dressed in red cotton shorts, white shirt and raincoat, 20in. high. £580

A Chad Valley doll of Winston Churchill, the moulded rubber head with painted facial features, 14in. £55

Simon & Halbig/Kammer & Reinhardt bisque-headed doll, 1914-27, 26in. high. £470

A ventriloquist's dummy modelled as a school girl with moving eyes and lower jaw, in original gym slip and skirt, 34in. high. £110

114

DOLLS

A bisque headed bebe with closed mouth, pierced ears and fixed blue yeux fibres, 10in. high. £1,320

A Simon & Halbig bisque headed Jutta character doll, impressed 'Jutta 1914 12', circa 1920, 21in. high. £440

A bisque headed child doll with blue sleeping eyes, pierced ears and fair mohair wig, 17in. high, marked Simon & Halbig. £440

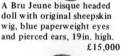

An early Alt, Beck & Gottshalck bisque shoulder and head doll, with painted facial features, 12in. high. £77

A set of Madame Alexander Dionne Quins, in original romper suits, bonnets, shoes and socks, 7in. high, marked Alexander. £495

A Bru Jeune bisque headed doll with original sheepskin wig, blue paperweight eyes and pierced ears, 19in. high. £15,000

Schoenau and Hoffmeister 'Princess Elizabeth' bisque headed doll impressed Porzellanfabrik Burggrub Princess Elizabeth 6½ Made in Germany, 23in. high. £480

A bisque laughing walking doll with the walking talking mechanism concealed under original outfit of blue and cream lace, 9in. high, marked with Gebruder Heubach Square. £264

A bisque headed doll, impressed SFBJ 236 Paris 12, with composition toddler body, circa 1910, 24in. high. £600

A Lenci fabric boy doll with short fair mohair wig, painted brown eyes and features, 14in. high. £440

A good Edwardian pedlar doll on ebonised stand under glass dome, the wax covered boy sailor standing on his one leg. £260

A bisque headed googlie eyed doll, with water melon mouth, brown mohair wig, and painted shoes and socks, 7in. high. £528

Simon and Halbig bisque headed doll, having brown sleeping eyes, open mouth with two moulded upper teeth, 23½in. high. £300

A pair of poured wax portrait dolls, modelled as Edward VII and Queen Alexandra, 21in. high, by Pierotti. £1,100

A cloth doll with black button eyes, painted facial features and stuffed body, in Highland dress, 10in. £33

An Armand Marseille bisque doll, with sleeping blue eyes, brown wig and cream apron and hat, 10in. high. £61

Danel et Cie bisque headed doll impressed E5D Depose with fixed blue glass eyes, painted mouth, fair hair wig, 16in. high. £450

A Lenci fabric boy doll with fair mohair wig and painted brown eyes looking right, 18in. high. £600

A Lenci fabric girl doll with fair mohair wig and painted brown eyes looking left, 12in. high. £380

J. D. Kestner bisque headed 'Hilda' doll, with combed hair, open mouth and upper moulded teeth, 20½in. long. £1,300

A composition mask faced googlie eyed doll, with smiling watermelon mouth, wearing spotted dress, 10½in. high. £330

A composition character headed doll modelled as Lord Kitchener, in original clothes with Sam Browne hat and puttees, 19in. high. £164

A pair of advertising dolls modelled as the 'Bisto Kids', designed by Will Owen, 11in. high, circa 1948. £209

A Kammer and Reinhardt bisque headed character doll, the jointed composition body dressed in red cotton dress, 12½in. high. £1,000

A bisque headed child doll with blue lashed sleeping eyes, pierced ears and blonde mohair wig, 20in. high, marked S & H K*R 50. £660

A Simon & Halbig mulatto bisque doll, with open mouth and upper teeth, 10in. high. £165

A painted felt doll dressed in the costume of Sicily, 15in. high, marked on foot, by Lenci, circa 1941. £187

A late 19th century fan with ivory sticks, the leaf of Brussels point de gaze, 35cm. long, in original box inscribed J. Duvelleroy, London. £380

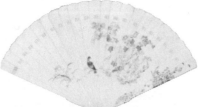

A late 19th century Japanese ivory brise fan with black, red and gold lacquer decoration of a pair of birds amidst rocks and flowers, 28cm. long. circa 1870's. £1,700

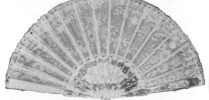

A late 19th century fan with carved, pierced mother-of-pearl sticks, designed with sprays of flowers, in a box, circa 1880's 30.5cm. long. £600

A fan, the shaped leaf painted with a woman wearing a violet trimmed bonnet, signed Jebagnes, 9½in., circa 1905. £1,650

A French fan designed as a peacock, signed A. Tomasse, the reverse inscribed Duvelleroy, in a box labelled Duvelleroy, circa 1900's, 25.5cm. long. £340

An Almanac fan for 1899, the leaf with vignettes of putti and garlands of flowers, and printed with a calendar of Saints' days, 10in., published by Dugrenot, Paris. £121

A 19th century painted fan, the guards inlaid with green enamel, porcelain plaques, semi-precious stones and pearls, probably French, 11¼in. long. £502

A black lace fan of Chantilly type lace, worked with two putti painting by a gazebo, with horn sticks, 13½in., circa 1890. £418

BEDS

A Gustav Stickley spindle-sided baby's crib, no. 919, circa 1907, 56½in. long. £833

Victorian brass and iron bed, 1875. £135

Mission oak double bed with exposed tenons, circa 1907, 58½in. wide. £1,351

One of a pair of mahogany Mission oak beds, possibly Roycroft, circa 1912, 42in. wide. £406

Late 19th century ebonised Bentwood cradle, Europe,. 52in. long. £625

An L. & J. G. Stickley slatted double-bed, signed with red (Handcraft) decal, 58in. wide. £5,952

A Wylie and Lockhead mahogany bed, the design attributed to George Logan, the toprail inlaid with mother-of-pearl and wood peacock-eye motifs, 122cm. high. £580

An English Art Deco Egyptian style bed, the tall headboard with beaten copper panel of Egyptian style foliage, 108cm. wide. £550

A small inlaid oak Heal's double bed, the design attributed to Ambrose Heal, with panelled footboard, 148cm. across. £850

119

BOOKCASES

A Sidney Barnsley walnut bookcase on two stepped trestle ends, 106.8cm. wide. £7,700

A Gustav Stickley V-top bookrack, signed with red decal in a box, 1902-04, 31in. wide, 31in. high. £833

Victorian, American walnut bookcase, the top section with two glazed doors, 3ft. 9in. wide. £500

A Gustav Stickley two-door bookcase with keyed tenons, no. 716, 42½in. high. £1,562

An Arts & Crafts oak bookcase, the cupboard doors with copper hinges, 101.3cm. wide. £374

A rare and important Gustav Stickley inlaid two door bookcase, designed by Harvey Ellis, circa 1903-1904, signed with red decal in a box, 55¾in. wide. £27,428

L. & J. G. Stickley single door bookcase, circa 1907, the single door with sixteen panes, signed with Handcraft decal, 30in. wide. £1,857

A Morris & Co. oak bookstand, the sloping rectangular rest surmounted with carved and turned ball and foliate finials, above panelled sides and open recess, 185.5cm. wide. £4,400

A late 19th century mahogany breakfront bookcase, the fitted adjustable shelves enclosed by four panel doors, 8ft.6in. high. £1,450

BOOKCASES

A grain painted wall shelf with scalloped sides, New England, circa 1840, 25½in. wide. £952

L. & J. G. Stickley single door bookcase with keyed tenons, no. 641, circa 1906, 36in. wide. £1,500

Gustav Stickley open slat-sided bookshelf, circa 1909, 27in. wide. £560

An ormolu mounted plum pudding mahogany dwarf open bookcase of Louis XVI style, on toupie feet, stamped Krieger, third quarter, 19th century, 22in. wide. £1,320

A late Victorian carved oak library bookcase with brass drop handles, fielded panelled doors and plinth base, 130in. wide. £1,300

An Edwardian satinwood revolving bookcase, on stand with cabriole legs and platform stretcher, 46cm. £1,600

A late Victorian walnut library bookcase, by Maple & Co., 183cm. wide. £1,000

A late 19th century 12ft. wide breakfront bookcase, enclosed by six glazed panel doors with pilaster supports. £4,600

A two-door bookcase, with mitred mullions, by Gustav Stickley, circa 1902-03, 35½in. wide. £3,243

BUREAUX

An ormolu mounted king-
wood, tulipwood and
marquetry bureau de dame
of bombe outlines, on
tapering cabriole legs, late
19th century, 31½in. wide.
£6,160

1930's oak bureau bookcase
with glazed top.   £250

Early 20th century oak
bureau.   £250

A George III style satinwood
bureau painted in naturalistic
colours in the manner of
Angelica Kauffmann, 36in.
£1,540

An Edwardian mahogany inlaid
bureau bookcase with two glazed
doors, on bracket feet, 39in.
wide.   £1,650

A 19th century chinoiserie
laquered bureau, in the 18th
century manner, the top and
fall-front decorated with a
Chinese riverscape, 92cm.
£1,250

Late 19th century ormolu
mounted marquetry and
trellis parquetry bureau a
cylindre with musical trophy,
44in. wide.   £3,000

A Gustav Stickley drop-
front desk, the doors opening to reveal a fitted interior,
circa 1906, 38in. wide. £1,666

An Edwardian inlaid maho-
gany cylinder bureau with
decorated urn front, 30in.
wide.   £525

BUREAUX

An Art Deco plastic veneered lady's bureau, the drop front enclosing compartments with single drawer below, 64cm. across. **£800**

An Edwardian mahogany fall-front bureau with rosewood crossbandings, 2ft.6in. wide. **£260**

A late 19th century rosewood and kingwood banded bonheur de jour, the whole decorated with floral marquetry and gilt metal mounts, 78cm. **£750**

Gustav Stickley drop-front desk with cabinet doors, circa 1902-04, 32¾in. wide. **£2,587**

Edwardian mahogany inlaid bureau bookcase, shell inlay on fall-front, 35in. wide. **£750**

A Sheraton Revival rosewood and marquetry small cylinder desk, 28in. wide. **£1,200**

Early 20th century Jacobean-style oak secretary, 30½in. wide. **£513**

1930's walnut veneered bureau on short cabriole legs, with fitted interior. **£50**

An Edwardian satinwood, harewood and foliate marquetry cylinder bureau, the rectangular top with a mirror backed brass galleried superstructure, 35in. **£2,200**

CABINETS

An Art Nouveau stained wood cabinet carved with tulips and ducks, 4ft.8in. high. £470

A Gordon Russell walnut side cabinet, with open top shelf above a panelled door enclosing shelves, 76cm. high. £360

Edwardian inlaid mahogany music cabinet having four drawers, all with fall fronts, and brass loop handles, 1ft. 8¾in. wide. £265

A Gustav Stickley work cabinet, circa 1905-7, with two cabinet doors over two drawers with square wooden pulls, 36in. high. £8,000

A large oak buffet designed by M. H. Baillie-Scott, the shaped rectangular top above shaped superstructure with beaten repousse copper panel, with three adjustable candle holders and small shelf flanked by two shaped cupboards, 327.9cm. wide. £3,520

A 19th century Oriental side cabinet with mother-of-pearl inlaid panels. £600

Late 19th century Kinji cabinet decorated in gold hiramakie, hirame and nashiji and inlaid in Shibayama style, 20.8cm. high. £4,180

A Japanese hardwood cabinet, 19th century, on block legs, mounted with engraved brass plaques and paktong lock, 40in. high. £1,331

A fine Aesthetic Movement ebony and lacquer cabinet, set with lacquered rosewood panels of Japanese landscapes with parquetry borders, stamped Gregory & Co. 212 & 214, Regent St., London 944, 202cm. high. £1,870

FURNITURE

CABINETS

A good Art Deco sycamore cocktail cabinet, the twin doors with rounded corners enclosing two recessed shelves, 91.7cm. wide. £1,450

A Rowley walnut and marquetry cabinet and stand, the design attributed to Frank Brangwyn, with two marquetry panels inlaid in various fruitwoods with toiling farm labourers, 85.1cm. wide. £770

An Edwardian rosewood inlaid side cabinet, 54in. wide. £750

One of a pair of late 19th century ormolu mounted ebonised side cabinets, 28½in. wide. £2,750

An Austrian Secessionist black lacquer and pewter inlaid cabinet, the shaped rectangular top above bowed and glazed cupboard door enclosing red stained interior, 161.6cm. wide. £5,500

An Arts & Crafts oak cabinet with repousse hammered copper panels, circa 1900, 31¾in. wide. £540

A side cabinet, the chromium plated metal frame supporting two walnut shelves, 125cm. wide. £220

A J. P. White oak inlaid dwarf cabinet designed by M. H. Baillie-Scott, the rectangular top above open recess with pierced sides and a cupboard door, 50.8cm. wide. £2,420

A late Victorian black and gilt japanned papier-mache purdonium, on later rosewood bracket feet, 18¾in. wide. £1,100

DINING CHAIRS

One of a set of six late Victorian painted satinwood side chairs, with bowed padded seats and turned tapering legs. £2,310

Two of a set of six 20th century Adirondack splint seat chairs, one armchair and five sidechairs, 38in. high. £296

Shaker maple tilter ladder-back sidechair with rush seat, circa 1875, 39½in. high. £375

A French Art Nouveau oak dining chair, designed by C. Plumet and A. Selmersheim. £340

Two of a set of eight 20th century inlaid mahogany Hepplewhite style chairs, America. £1,970

One of a pair of birch laminated side chairs by Gerald Summers. £3,740

An Adirondack hickory chair, probably New York, early 20th century, stick construction with six spindles in back and twelve in seat. £227

Two of a set of five Gustav Stickley dining chairs with rush seats, circa 1907, 37in. high. £1,062

A rush-seated oak sidechair, by Joseph P. McHugh & Co., N.Y., circa 1900, 36in. high. £187

DINING CHAIRS

A Serrurier-Bovy 'Silex' dismantling mahogany chair, circa 1905.   £216

Two of a set of five rosewood mahogany and marquetry inlaid occasional chairs, circa 1900.   £775

One of a set of four late Victorian mahogany framed dining chairs with shaped front supports.   £300

One of a pair of side chairs designed by Josef Hoffmann, the rounded rectangular backs and seats upholstered in black and grey woollen fabric.   £880

One of a set of five Dutch elm dining chairs and an armchair of similar design, late 19th century and later.   £1,760

'Military chair' by Gerrit Rietveld, the white painted rectangular back and seat on black painted bar frame, on rectangular section legs.   £11,000

One of a pair of English Art Deco walnut painted Egyptian style side chairs, the rectangular backs with leather upholstered tablet top rails.   £935

Two of a set of eight mahogany inlaid chairs, Edwardian. £1,900

One of a pair of Wylie and Lockhead beech chairs, possibly designed by E.A. Taylor, tapering supports united by stretchers.   £160

FURNITURE

EASY CHAIRS

A wicker patio chair designed by Terence Conran.   £88

A blue PVC inflatable armchair.   £378

One of a pair of Barcelona chairs, designed by Mies van der Rohe, with stainless steel, X-shaped frames.   £770

L. & J. G. Stickley fixed back armchair, circa 1912, with upholstered spring cushion seat with back cushion, unsigned, 32in. high.   £2,714

A Herman Miller laminated rosewood lounge chair designed by Charles Eames, upholstered in black hide, on swivel, five-pronged, aluminium base.   £825

A Gustav Stickley willow armchair, circa 1910, the tall back with square cut-outs centred by flat arms, unsigned, 42¾in. high.   £2,000

An upholstered oak armchair with cut out sides, circa 1905, 28¾in. wide.   £699

Late 19th century wing easy chair with reclining action.   £500

A mahogany bergere with rectangular caned back and seat in a channelled frame, late 19th century.   £495

EASY CHAIRS

A Victorian woven canework rocking armchair. **£120**

A Gustav Stickley bent arm spindle Morris chair, circa 1907, with spring cushion seat. **£7,738**

One of a pair of Italian perspex and chromium plated tubular steel chairs, designed by Harvey Guzzini, with original label. **£330**

A Morris & Co. oak armchair to a design by Philip Webb, with horizontal spindles and arms supported by turned beaded spindles. **£1,400**

A Gustav Stickley bird's-eye maple wide slat cube chair, circa 1903-04, no. 328. **£1,785**

A small Art Deco gilt and up-holstered salon chair attri-buted to Jules Leleu, the curved back and arm rests upholstered in beige fabric. **£1,540**

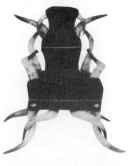

An adjustable back armchair, attributed to J. Young & Co., circa 1910, 31½in. wide. **£476**

Late 19th century Victorian steer horn armchair, uphol-stered in maroon velvet, America. **£909**

An adjustable gothic oak arm-chair, designed by Charles Bevan, with upholstered back and seat with crossed sides. **£620**

ELBOW CHAIRS

A walnut rocking chair, by G. Hunzinger, N.Y., circa 1876, 32in. high. £174

One of a set of six Macassar ebony Art Deco armchairs, attributed to Paul Kiss, upholstered in brown hide. £6,050

A laminated mahogany armchair, circa 1900, 45in. high. £354

A child's spindle back arm rocker, unsigned, circa 1915, 24¼in. high. £202

A tall spindle-back armchair, no. 386, by Gustav Stickley, 49½in. high. £6,486

One of a pair of oak Bentwood open armchairs, each bearing a label 'Patent Pending 25597/1932, Regd Design 781, 637. £340

A Gustav Stickley spindlesided cube chair, no. 391, circa 1907, 26in. wide. £9,523

A Plail Bros. barrel-back armchair, Wayland, N.Y., circa 1910, 33in. high. £562

An oak and oak veneered armchair with scenic inlay, circa 1910, unsigned, 37in. high. £756

ELBOW CHAIRS

A stained wood and embossed leather Art Nouveau chair, circular panelled seat with brass studs, on square legs joined by stretchers. £550

An Italian parcel gilt and painted rocking chair, the arms and rectangular seat on supports in the form of lions, late 19th century, labelled Countess of North Brook. £1,980

An oak framed chair with carved narrow back and shaped arms. £360

One of a pair of laminated birchwood open armchairs designed by Gerald Summers, with central splat and curvilinear armrests. £14,300

An important oak lath armchair designed by Marcel Breuer for the Bauhaus, Weimar, 1924, constructed from vertical and horizontal strips of stained oak, 94.8cm. high. £28,600

Part of a suite of Scandinavian cream and green painted furniture in the revived neo-classical style, circa 1880. £2,750

One of a set of six Wiener Werkstatte black stained limed oak dining chairs, designed by J. Hoffmann. £17,600

A Gimson design yew-wood adjustable ladder back open arm chair, with shaped crossrails. £520

An Arts & Crafts inlaid oak elbow chair, the central back splat inlaid with a flower motif in pewter and wood. £120

CHESTS OF DRAWERS

Late 19th century wood tansu in two parts, 118.5cm. wide. £990

A Gustav Stickley chest-of-drawers, no. 901, with wooden pulls, circa 1907, 37in. wide. £773

A Betty Joel Art Deco burr walnut chest of drawers, with six short drawers, on four short fluted legs of rectangular-section, 71cm. wide. £440

Victorian satinwood and mahogany chest with poker-work inlay. £400

An Edwardian satinwood serpentine fronted collector's chest of ten graduated drawers, 17in. wide. £500

1930's oak chest of four drawers with blind fret decoration and turned wooden knobs. £50

An Army and Navy oak military chest with inset brass bindings and handles, on turned feet, 45in. wide, circa 1900. £820

A Gustav Stickley nine-drawer tall chest, no. 913, circa 1907, 36in. wide, 50in. high. £2,500

A Victorian walnut chest, the drawers with wood knob handles, 3ft.11in. wide. £240

CUPBOARDS

A fine quality rosewood and inlaid chiffonier, the main bevelled mirror plate flanked by subsidiary arched mirrors and inlaid panels, circa 1890, 56in. wide.   £1,100

Late 19th century mahogany pot cupboard with carved and panelled door.   £60

One of a pair of Austrian oak and leaded glass cupboards, 197.9cm. high, 103.6cm. wide.
£858

An Edwardian satinwood and kingwood banded corner cabinet painted with trailing foliage in naturalistic colours, on square tapered legs, 36in. wide.   £5,280

An ormolu mounted king-wood and marquetry commode a encoignures after the model by J.H. Riesener, on massive foliate sabots headed by foliate panels, circa 1900, 80in. wide.
£9,350

An Edwardian mahogany and satinwood inlaid standing corner cupboard, with broken arch pediment, 70cm. wide.   £1,400

An English oak corner buffet, circa 1900, 111cm. wide.   £216

An Edward Barnsley walnut corner cabinet with ebony stringing and panelled fall flap, on stepped plinth, circa 1930, 126.3cm. wide.   £5,280

Chinese objets d'art display cabinet, circa 1890-1900.
£4,400

DISPLAY CABINETS

A Louis Majorelle Art Nouveau walnut and rosewood vitrine, 188cm. high. £2,600

A Victorian rococo style mahogany side cabinet with arch top oblong mirror panel back, 5ft. wide. £1,100

An Art Deco mahogany, maple and chromium plated display cabinet, on solid mahogany side supports united by an undertier. £1,000

A Limbert single door china cabinet, no. 1347, Grand Rapids, Michigan, circa 1907, 34¼in. wide. £1,027

An Art Nouveau mahogany display cabinet, with recessed top shelf held by front supports heavily carved with fruit and leaves, 106.8cm. across. £750

An Edwardian satinwood display cabinet, the front with central glazed panel flanked by bowed glazed doors, 42in. wide. £990

A French kingwood Vernis Martin vitrine of small size with shaped sides and front, late 19th century, 29in. wide. £2,530

An Art Deco walnut veneered circular display cabinet, with glazed doors enclosing glass shelves, 120.5cm. high. £300

Edwardian carved mahogany display cabinet with demi-lune display shelf, 30in. wide. £725

DISPLAY CABINETS

Sheraton Revival mahogany glazed china cabinet, 3ft. wide.   £440

Art Nouveau style oak display cabinet.   £284

An Edwardian mahogany display cabinet inlaid with ribbon-tied bellflowers and foliage, on cabriole legs, 79in. high.   £600

An Edwardian mahogany display cabinet inlaid with cornucopias, scrolling foliage, urns and patera, on tapering square supports joined by an undertier, 83in. high.
£2,300

Mission oak two-door china closet, no. 2017, circa 1910, 46½in. wide.   £218

A Christopher Pratt & Sons inlaid mahogany display cabinet, 192.6cm. high.
£825

A Wylie & Lochhead mahogany display cabinet, designed by E. A. Taylor, 88cm. wide.   £1,728

An Edwardian mahogany display cabinet crossbanded in satinwood, 57½in. wide.
£1,350

An Edwardian mahogany display cabinet outlined with satinwood banding, boxwood and ebony stringing, 35¾in. wide.   £750

135

KNEEHOLE DESKS

A desk, the top suspended on tubular steel U-shaped supports, with cantilever chair, desk 164.4cm.wide. £770

An English Arts & Crafts brass mounted mahogany, sycamore and walnut marquetry partner's desk, 129.6cm. wide. £2,484

An early John Makepeace, Andaman padouk and leather-covered desk, by M. Doughty, D. Pearson and A. Freeman, 199cm. wide, and a chair. £1,980

A French Art Deco beechwood writing desk on trestle ends, 105.4cmwide. £605

An ormolu mounted mahogany pedestal desk of Empire style, the eared rectangular top inset with green leather, on turned feet, circa 1880, 56in. wide. £4,180

An Edwardian mahogany kneehole pedestal desk, inlaid with satinwood and fluted bands, with boxwood line borders, 48in. £880

A Victorian mahogany kneehole desk with raised gallery, having three drawers to each side and a cupboard to the kneehole, 45in. wide. £580

Oak twin pedestal roll-top desk, 1900. £729

A Heal's sycamore kneehole desk, the rectangular top with semi-circular end, 133.4cm. wide. £440

An Arts and Crafts oak framed fire screen, the plain oak frame having a toprail pierced with oval shapes, 77.4cm. high. £95

A wrought-iron and pierced copper fire-screen, circa 1900, 34½in. wide. £162

20th century wrought iron firescreen in the gothic style. £35

A late Victorian scrapwork four-leaf screen with coloured figures and scenes, each leaf 66½ x 22¼in. £880

A late 19th century French gilt metal framed fireguard, the oval glass panel painted with trailing roses. £143

A late Victorian ebonised, parcel gilt and scrapwork three-leaf screen, each leaf 70 x 23¾in. £1,540

An Aesthetic Movement ebonised and painted three-leaf screen, 134.2cm. wide, 143.9cm. high. £825

A late Victorian walnut four leaf screen, each leaf incorporating two arched scrapwork panels depicting contemporary literary figures and aristocracy, each leaf 32 x 79in., dated 1885 and initialled J.F. £4,620

An inlaid oak three-panelled screen, designed by Harvey Ellis for Gustav Stickley, circa 1903-04, 66¾in. high, each panel 20in. wide. £10,714

SECRETAIRES

Late 19th century Wooton's Patent desk of walnut and burr walnut, 39½in. wide. £4,400

A Heal's oak writing desk, designed by Ambrose Heal, 152.3cm. wide. £2,640

A Victorian walnut roll-top desk, Winneberger, Penn., circa 1890, 40½in. wide. £709

A Heals red lacquered bureau cabinet, the fall flap enclosing fitted interior of eight pigeon-holes and two small drawers, on four turned feet, circa 1918, 76.5cm. wide. £440

A late Victorian rosewood davenport, inlaid with marquetry and geometric box-wood lines, on square splayed tapering legs, 23in. wide. £682

An Edwardian mahogany and satinwood inlaid sec-retaire bookcase, the two panel doors with oval patera of musical muses, 91cm. wide. £3,200

Gustav Stickley oak and wrought iron secretary, desig-ned by Harvey Ellis, circa 1904, 56in. wide. £9,090

An Edwardian rosewood and inlaid writing and work table, designed by John Bagshaw & Son, inlaid with flowers and leafage, 26½in. £1,650

An inlaid oak secretary, designed by Harvey Ellis for Gustav Stickley, circa 1903-04, 42in. wide. £55,357

138

SECRETAIRES

A lady's oak desk with fall-front, circa 1890, 28½in. wide. £320

Attractive Edwardian mahogany escritoire, with cock-beading to drawer fronts and circular brass drop handles, original keys, 37in. wide. £800

An Edwardian mahogany writing table, interior fitted with a rising stationery rack and drawers, 26in. high. £2,035

Late 19th century marquetry secretaire with pull-out secretary drawer, Holland, 41½in. wide. £875

A late Victorian rosewood davenport, inlaid with ivory marquetry and geometric lines. £990

A German oak green stained writing desk in the style of C. A. Voysey, 110.5cm. wide. £3,520

An Ernest Gimson walnut bureau cabinet on stand, circa 1906, 99.5cm. wide. £11,000

Shop-O'-The-Crafters slant front desk, Ohio, circa 1906, style no. 279, signed with paper label, 42in. wide. £281

A good Edwardian mahogany secretaire chest of small proportions, on splayed bracket feet, 33½in. wide. £2,200

SETTEES & COUCHES

'Anfibio', a white leather upholstered sofa bed designed by Alessandro Becchi, 240cm. wide.
£594

'Djinn series', an upholstered chaise longue designed by Olivier Mourgue, in green nylon stretch jersey, circa 1965, 170cm. long. £756

A tubular chromium plated chaise longue designed by Le Corbusier and Charlotte Perriand, the adjustable seat upholstered in brown and white pony skin. £2,420

Pine bench, probably circa 1900. £260

A Gustav Stickley tall spindleback settee, no. 286, signed with decal, circa 1906, 48in. wide.
£21,428

An Art Nouveau mahogany and marquetry settle on three arched trestle supports, circa 1890, 185cm. wide. £990

A three seater Gimson design yew settee, having drop-in rush seat, on bobbin supports.
£1,350

An early Gustav Stickley settle with arched slats, 1901-03, 60in. wide. £16,071

SETTEES & COUCHES

Rare L. & J. G. Stickley spindle 'Prairie' settle, circa 1912, no. 234 the broad even sided flat crest rail over spindles, two section seat, unsigned, 86in. wide. £48,571

'Boxing Glove', a chaise longue, by De Sede, the frame upholstered and covered in brown and beige leather, 173cm. long. £2,700

A 'Lip' sofa after a design by Salvador Dali, upholstered in red nylon stretch fabric, 209cm. wide. £1,512

Chaise longue upholstered in black leather, designed by Le Corbusier, 1926. £310

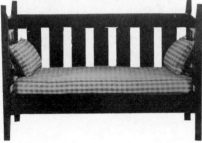

A Gustav Stickley slat-back settle, no. 206, circa 1904-06, 60in. wide. £8,928

A Morris & Co. ebonised and rush settle, the rectangular turned back and arms above rectangular rush seat, on eight turned legs, 122cm. wide. £352

An Edwardian open arm two seater settee, having inlaid and buttoned upholstered back and stuffover seat. £420

A Stickley Bros. slat-back settle, signed with paper label, Quaint, circa 1910, 72in. wide. £2,432

SIDEBOARDS

A good ebonised and painted sideboard, the painted panels attributed to Henry Stacy Marks, on turned supports and painted with gilt stylised borders, 198cm.long. £3,200

An Edwardian mahogany serpentine-fronted sideboard, in the Sheraton manner, on square section tapered legs. £2,400

A Limbert mirrored sideboard, no. 1453 3/4, circa 1910, 48in. wide. £296

A Limbert sideboard with arched mirrored backboard with corbel detail, Michigan, circa 1910, 47¾in. wide. £648

Late 19th century carved teak sideboard, China, 48in. wide. £875

A Gordon Russell oak and chestnut sideboard, with chestnut tapering handles, shaped apron below, on octagonal supports, 1927, cabinet maker P. J. Wade, 4ft.5½in. wide. £1,700

SIDEBOARDS

Early Gustav Stickley sideboard, no. 967, with long copper strap hardware and square copper pulls, 60in. wide. £5,650

A Stickley Bros. sideboard, Grand Rapids, Michigan, 1912, 60in. wide. £265

A Gustav Stickley oak sideboard with open plate rack, circa 1905-06, 49in. wide. £773

A large sideboard cabinet, the cupboard over with scroll fret carved doors and brass lion mask and drop ring handles, 7ft.10in.high. £1,034

An unusual 6ft. serpentine fronted oak sideboard, richly inlaid with satinwood and rosewood chequer work, 7ft.3in. high. £1,050

An eight-legged sideboard, model no. 961, plate rail with V-board panelled back, by Gustav Stickley, circa 1902-04, 70in. wide. £2,027

FURTURE

STANDS

1930's oak framed corner umbrella stand. £20

A polished chromium hat stand made for Bazzi in Milan, 51.6cm. high. £453

Late 19th century Eastlake folio stand. £720

Gustav Stickley inlaid tiger maple open music stand, circa 1904, no. 670, signed with Eastwood label, 39in. high. £5,069

Art Nouveau style oak umbrella stand on gutta feet. £75

A three-tiered muffin stand, by Charles Rohlfs, Buffalo, N.Y., 1907, 34in. high. £702

A Gordon Russell walnut linen bag and frame, with a linen bag suspended within, 82.5cm. high. £320

A Gustav Stickley three-drawer bedside stand, style no. 842, copper hardware with loop handles, circa 1907, 29½in. high. £763

An L. & J. G. Stickley magazine rack, no. 45, circa 1912, 44½in. high. £812

STANDS

A Bentwood hall stand, possibly made by Thoret and possibly designed by Josef Hoffman, 194.5cm. high.
£550

A late 19th century fruitwood sewing accessory stand with table clamp stay.   £140

A drink stand, by L. & J. G. Stickley, no. 587, circa 1912, 16in. sq.   £351

A Gustav Stickley slat-sided folio stand, no. 551, 1902-03, 40½in. high, 29½in. wide.   £1,785

A marquetry panelled oak smoking rack, possibly Stickley Bros., Michigan, circa 1910, style no. 264-100, 22in. high, 24in. wide.   £81

Early 20th century Mission oak magazine stand with cut out arched sides, 49in. high.   £312

An ebonised hardwood Oriental jardiniere stand with inset rouge marble top.   £340

A cane-sided plant stand, probably Limbert, circa 1910, 23in. high, the top 16in. sq.   £282

An L. & J. G. Stickley slat-sided magazine rack, no. 46, circa 1910, signed with decal, 42in. high.   £1,312

STOOLS

A Stickley Bros. spindle sided footstool, circa 1907, with stretchers centering seven spindles each side, unsigned, 20½in. wide. £1,485

A Herman Miller laminated rosewood ottoman designed by Charles Eames, upholstered in black hide. £385

An English Art Deco walnut and painted Egyptian style stool, the rectangular concave seat upholstered in brown leather. £264

One of a pair of Liberty oak folding stools, each consisting of ten slats forming X-shaped frames. £242

Victorian rosewood stool on cabriole legs with scroll feet and brass castors, 18in. square. £230

A small Liberty & Co. oak 'Thebes' stool, the shaped seat supported on three splayed legs, with Liberty & Co. label. £220

A Liberty & Co. 'Thebes' stool, the square shallow seat with pierced panels on four turned and waisted legs. £209

Late 19th century pottery garden seat, probably France, whimsically depicting a cushion resting on a basket, 20in. high. £528

A 19th century Continental carved giltwood rectangular stool covered in floral material. £520

STOOLS

A Gustav Stickley upholstered footstool with tacked leather surface, no. 300, circa 1905, 20½in. wide. £952

A Gustav Stickley piano bench, no. 217, plank sides with D-shaped handles, circa 1907, 36in. long. £476

A Liberty and Co. oak stool with square curved seat, on straight square section legs joined by plain stretchers and diagonal struts. £605

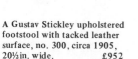

An Art Deco stained black and limed oak Ashanti style stool, possibly French, on five turned supports, 51.5cm. high. £240

A Gordon Russell walnut and ebony stool with shaped eared handles, on octagonal section legs with ebony chamfered bulbous feet. £3,630

A Derby & Co. oak window seat, the cut-out armrests with spindle supports, circa 1910, 28in. high. £432

Early 20th century octagonal oak garden seat, unsigned, 16in. diam. £265

A Barcelona chromium plated stool designed by Mies van der Rohe, with curved cross legs. £130

A tabouret with cut corners, by L. & J. G. Stickley, no. 560, circa 1912, 16in. wide. £405

SUITES

Early 20th century Plail & Co., barrel-back settee and matching armchairs, 46¼in. long.
£2,857

An Edwardian mahogany drawingroom suite of seven pieces, with satinwood panel and boxwood string inlay. £450

An Art Nouveau pearwood salon suite, comprising a three seater settee, 175cm. long, two elbow chairs and four upright chairs. £2,600

SUITES

A 19th century three piece beech frame drawing room suite, in the Louis XVI manner, on turned and fluted tapering legs, 185cm. £1,600

An Edwardian mahogany and boxwood strung five-piece salon suite.
£1,100

Part of a four-piece Harden & Co. livingroom set, comprising: settee, rocker and two armchairs, settee 54in. wide, circa 1910. £1,104

CARD TABLES

Late Victorian mahogany octagonal top occasional table inlaid with ebony and boxwood on turned supports with undertier. **£125**

A 19th century red tortoiseshell boulle fold-over card table, over bold cabriole legs headed by female masks, 95cm. **£900**

An Edwardian rosewood envelope-top card table, each flap inlaid with bowls of fruit, cornucopiae and scrolling foliage, 23¾in. square. **£1,500**

A fine Edwardian rosewood envelope card table with bone and boxwood inlay, on four squared tapering supports, 21½in. square. **£880**

A rosewood and boxwood strung card table, the rectangular, hinged top, centred by an inlaid oval, stamped 'Maple & Co.', circa 1900, 36in. wide. **£1,200**

Edwardian inlaid mahogany hexagonal top occasional table with undertier and brass castors. **£100**

Late 19th century mahogany occasional table with shaped stretchers. **£100**

A fine quality George III style satinwood demi-lune card table, on square tapered legs, 35½in. wide, circa 1890. **£1,400**

Late 19th century mahogany shaped top occasional table on six legs with fret cut supports and undertier. **£200**

CENTRE TABLES

Late 19th century Renaissance
Revival inlaid mahogany centre
table, America, 45½in. wide. £620

A Salvatore Meli ceramic
and glass centre table,
120.5cm. wide.   £7,150

A Victorian figured walnut
occasional table with double
serpentine shaped top, circa
1880, 47in. long.   £940

An Italian giltwood and
pietra dura centre table,
ink label beneath stretcher
'Monsieur R. O. Milne
Florence 18.4.99', 26¾in.
wide.   £3,740

A Limbert octagonal table,
circa 1905, the overhanging top
on flat splayed legs with spade
cut-outs, 29¼in. high.   £800

A Morris & Co. walnut centre
table, 69cm. diam.   £495

An oak centre table framed
by chequered inlaid lines
executed by Peter Waals
assisted by P. Burchett, 1928,
68.3cm. wide.   £1,512

A Scandinavian green and
cream painted centre table in
the revived neo-classical
style, circa 1880, 47in. diam.
£3,080

An English Art Deco walnut
centre table, the octagonal top
on a pedestal base consisting of
four shaped rectangular compartments with open recesses, 70.5cm.
high.   £660

DINING TABLES

Victorian oak draw-leaf table, circa 1900. £175

20th century oak gateleg table with barley twist supports and half-round flaps. £75

1920's oak dining table. £200

An Art Deco walnut dining table, the rounded rectangular top with mirrored walnut veneer, on curved V-shaped trestle ends, 179.5cm. long. £660

A small Gordon Russell oak drop leaf gateleg occasional table with plank sides and pull-out supports, 51 x 82cm., extended. £650

Late 19th century mahogany Sutherland table with square flaps. £175

An oak drop-leaf table, no. 638, by Gustav Stickley, circa 1906, 42in. long extended. £1,135

Round pedestal base dining table, Hastings Co., Michigan, circa 1915, signed with decal on pedestal top, 54in. diam. £750

A Gustav Stickley hexagonal leather-top table, no. 624, circa 1910-12, 48in. diam. £4,166

DRESSING TABLES

An Art Deco mahogany dressing table, having three pivot domed mirrors, 130cm. wide. £620

An Arts & Crafts dressing table by George Walton, 134.2cm. wide. £605

Edwardian mahogany dressing table with cabriole shaped legs, circa 1910. £325

An Edwardian rosewood and inlaid dressing chest with swing mirror flanked by superstructure with drawers and shelves, on turned feet, 138cm. £1,000

Part of an Art Deco Macassar ebony bedroom suite, the dressing table 47in. across. £1,980

An Art Nouveau mahogany and inlaid dressing table with cartouche-shaped bevelled swing-frame mirror, 122cm. wide. £520

An Art Deco walnut dressing table, the removable shaped top having a glass cover and three drawers, 88cm. long. £90

A Peter Waals walnut dressing table with rectangular cheval mirror, 116.4cm. wide. £550

An Edwardian mahogany inlaid kidney dressing table with insert leather top and fitted with nine drawers, 48in. wide. £2,750

OCCASIONAL TABLES

An Edwardian mahogany nest of three oval tables on sabre legs. £290

A brushed steel and chromium-plated table, the design attributed to Ringo Starr, 121.5cm. wide, 66cm. high. £220

Late 19th century Moorish inlaid occasional table. £40

An ebonised occasional table by E.W.Godwin, on turned tapering legs united by an undertier, 66cm. high. £220

An occasional table with cut corners, possibly early Gustav Stickley, circa 1902-04, 29in. high. £594

An ormolu mounted king-wood and marquetry two tier Sutherland table, the two-eared sepentine rectangular twin flap tiers inlaid with sprigs of foliage, late 19th century, 31in. wide, open; 28¼in. high; 25¾in. deep. £3,740

A Gustav Stickley round leather-top table, no. 645, circa 1907, 36in. diam. £1,250

L. & J. G. Stickley oak server with open plate rack, circa 1912, no. 750, 48in. wide. £350

An occasional table, no. 609, by Gustav Stickley, circa 1904-05, unsigned, 36in. diam. £486

OCCASIONAL TABLES

A late Victorian mahogany specimen marble occasional table, 21in. wide. £1,980

A laminated beechwood two-tier low circular table designed by Gerald Summers for The Makers of Simple Furniture, 73.3cm. diam. £1,620

An Emile Galle oak and marquetry table a deux plateaux, 60.2cm. wide. £432

A Limbert oval table with cut-out sides, Grand Rapids, Michigan, circa 1907, no. 146, 45in. long. £648

A Galle mahogany and marquetry two-tier etagere, signed in the marquetry Galle, 59.3cm. wide. £1,836

A Finmar laminated birch two tier table, designed by Alvar Aalto, painted black, the rectangular tiers with curved sides supported by rounded square shaped trestle ends, printed manufacturer's label, 58.6cm. high; 60cm. wide; 50.1cm. deep. £285

An Art Deco coffee table, circular parquetry top on four scrolling wrought iron legs, 79.6cm. diam. £432

A Gustav Stickley table with twelve Grueby tiles, circa 1902-4, with four flat rails framing twelve four-inch green tiles, signed, 24in. wide. £16,571

A Limbert oval occasional table, style no. 146, circa 1907, 36in. long. £1,309

WRITING TABLES

An L. & J. G. Stickley drop-front writing desk, no. 613, writing surface with fitted interior, circa 1910, 32in. wide. £406

A late Victorian rosewood writing table, inlaid with marquetry arabesques, box-wood lines and bellflower festoons, on square tapering legs, 42in. £2,090

An Arts and Crafts writing table, the shaped superstructure with castellated back panel above a three-quarter gallery with over-hanging top, 111.2cm. wide. £495

An early Gustav Stickley chalet desk, circa 1901-2, the arched gallery top with pierced corner cut-outs and keyed tenon sides, 45¾in. high. £914

An Edwardian mahogany Carlton House writing table on square tapering legs, 45in. wide. £2,100

An Arts and Crafts oak writing cabinet, the shaped rectangular top with curved three-quarter gallery above open recess, fall flap and short drawers, 94cm. wide. £385

An inlaid oak drop-front desk, designed by Harvey Ellis for Gustav Stickley, 1903-04, style no. 706, 30in. wide. £11,904

A walnut writing table by Peter Waals, with barber's pole inlay, on moulded tapering legs, 94cm. wide. £1,870

A Carlo Bugatti ebonised and rosewood lady's writing desk with pewter and ivory inlay, 75.5cm. wide. £3,850

WARDROBES

Early 20th century mahogany gentleman's wardrobe with pressed brass handles and a plinth base. £300

An English Arts & Crafts walnut combination wardrobe with ebony crossbanding, 66in. wide. £340

20th century oak wardrobe with central oval mirror and Spanish feet. £50

An Arts and Crafts mahogany wardrobe, attributed to Kenton & Co., possibly to a design by Arthur Blomfield, the doors enclosing drawers and shelves, 149cm. wide. £500

A fine Art Nouveau walnut wardrobe, designed by Georges de Feure, with shaped and carved pediment above twin central panelled doors, 200cm. wide. £5,000

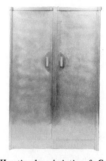

A Huntingdon Aviation & Co. aluminium wardrobe designed by P.W. Cow, with twin doors and amber plastic pulls, 122cm. across. £150

A Gustav Stickley two-door wardrobe, no. 920, 1904-06, 33in. wide. £1,845

An Arts & Crafts breakfront oak wardrobe by George Walton, 230.2cm. wide. £4,180

An Arts and Crafts oak wardrobe with broad everted top above a central mirrored door flanked by panelled sides, 198.5cm. high. £300

BOTTLES

'Figurines Avec Bouchon', a Lalique frosted glass bottle and stopper, 11½in. high. £950

A Venini glass bottle and stopper, swollen cylindrical, tall neck and spherical stopper, 1950's, 33.5cm. high. £250

A late Victorian cut glass square cologne bottle with a silver openwork mount by William Comyns, 5½in. high. £385

Three Vistosi tall bottle vases, designed by Peter Pelzel, circa 1960, 43.5cm., 41cm. and 34cm. £1,320

A Lalique clear and frosted glass bottle and stopper, the cylindrical body moulded with thorny branches, 4¼in. high. £385

A Galle oviform clear and enamelled glass bottle decanter with moulded flutes, 7¾in. high. £180

A Dimple Haig clear glass bottle, decorated with pierced plated mounts depicting Chinese dragons, original stopper, 10½in. high. £80

'Red Star/Stomach Bitters' bottle, fluted shoulder and base, amber, sloping collar, smooth base, 11½in. high, America, circa 1900. £128

A Galle enamelled glass bottle with silver stopper, circa 1900, 17.5cm. high. £1,430

BOWLS

Late 19th century Daum Nancy acid finished glass bowl, France, signed, 5in. diam.   £300

A Daum acid etched cameo bowl, the clear glass etched with poppies heightened with gilt decoration, 25cm. wide.
£495

Art glass bowl, attributed to Victor Durand, diam. 4¾in.
£55

Late 19th century two-part cut glass punch bowl, America, 14½in. high, 14¾in. diam.   £629

One of two Daum Cameo glass rosebowls, crimped ruffled rim decorated with cameo-cut sprays of violets, signed 'Daum/Nancy', diam. 7in.
£446

A Daum bowl, the white, green and red mottled glass acid-etched with primroses and foliage, 13.9cm. high.
£605

Late 19th century Venetian pedestal bowl in blotched pink and opaque white and clear aventurine glass, 10½in. high.   £180

A Burmese satin finished toothpick holder, Boston & Sandwich Glass Co., Mass., circa 1885, 1.7/8in. high.
£139

Late 19th century Bohemian rose bowl on stand, 16½in. high.   £760

BOWLS

An Austrian art glass bowl, of bright pink cased to opal with iridescent mauve interior, 5¼in. high. £192

A Loetz type art glass mounted centre bowl, of brilliant green with roundel texture and iridescent surface, 11in. high. £59

A green stained Lalique bowl, the clear and satin finished glass moulded with a pattern of birds and foliage, 23.4cm. diam. £286

A Daum cameo glass jardiniere, the mottled amber tinted body overlaid with two tones of ruby glass acid etched with exotic lilies and grasses, 25cm. £820

A Kosta glass bowl designed by Evald Dahlskog, with cut and engraved decoration of women on horseback, 16.5cm. high. £550

A large and colourful cased glass bowl by the American studio glass maker, Samuel J. Herman, 51.5cm. wide, inscribed and dated 1971. £820

A Loetz bowl, the bulbous body with a drawn trefoil rim, the clear glass internally decorated with a pattern of blue and glittery-green spots, 14.6cm. high. £286

A Daum acid etched and enamelled verrerie parlante ashtray, the clear and amber tinted glass with ribbon motto amid mistletoe on an acid textured ground, 14cm. diam. £462

An Orrefors footed bowl designed by Simon Gate and engraved by Wilhelm Eisert, 1932, the body with engraved decoration of two women in a constructivist city, 15cm. high. £990

BOWLS

A Loetz iridescent glass bowl with an everted rim and having six loop handles, exhibiting a green, gold and mauve iridescent skin, 21.3cm. diam.
£900

A Decorchemont pate-de-verre bowl, short cylindrical foot and straight sided flaring body, 6.5cm. high.
£1,430

A Galle enamelled glass bowl, the slightly smoky body acid etched with foliage, 15cm. wide.
£400

A Haida bowl and cover, the clear glass decorated with green, blue and red flowers, 12.5cm. high.
£198

An Austrian art glass metal mounted bowl, of brilliant yellow-green, mounted in four pronged bronzed metal holder, 10½in. high.
£73

An Orvit cameo glass, mounted punch bowl, cameo carved with four stylised designs of alternating grapes on vines and grape leaf clusters, 12in. high.
£887

An Austrian art glass bowl, of yellow-green iridescent glass decorated with red-purple threading, diam. 9½in.   £44

An Argy-Rousseau pate-de-verre bowl, with moulded decoration of three reserves with a ballerina in white taking her bow, surrounded by stylised rose border, on a mottled yellow ground, 6.3cm. high.   £3,520

A Tiffany Favrile intaglio cut bowl, with gold iridescence and pink and blue highlights, 9½in. diam.
£532

BOWLS

A Christopher Williams dust bowl, engraved The Glasshouse 1986, 30.5cm. diam. £462

Steuben centrepiece bowl with adjusting holder, diam. 12in. £265

A Decorchment pate-de-verre bowl, green and brown marbled glass, circa 1940, 25.7cm. wide. £1,620

'Limbo for Three', a David Prytherch sculpture bowl form, 1986, 38cm. high. £3,300

A silver mounted cut glass tazza, the dish with rosette motif, by Orest Kurliukov, Moscow, circa 1880, 7¾in. high, 531gr. without glass dish. £550

An amberina bride's basket and holder, set into a silver plated basket with applied leaves and cherries, 9in. high. £384

A Steven Newell bowl with decoration of Adam and Eve, 1986, 23.5cm. high. £2,420

Glossy Burmese bowl, star shaped form with fluted, ruffled rim, circa 1890, 2¼in. high. £139

A Lalique opalescent bowl, the blue opalescent glass moulded with a frieze of budgerigars, 24cm. diam. £1,760

BOXES

An early 20th century Galle glass box and cover, 3in. diam., signed.   £900

A clear and brown stained rectangular box, by Rene Lalique, 4in. wide.   £300

'Dahlia', a Lalique circular box and cover in clear and satin finished glass, 13.6cm. diam.   £432

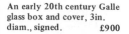

Square oak cased, 19th century, four bottle decanter box, having cast brass corner mounts and carrying handle.   £200

'Houppes'. A Lalique opalescent glass circular box and cover, moulded on the inside with powder-puffs, 14cm. diam.   £520

A Guild of Handicrafts silver and glass box and cover, designed by C. R. Ashbee, with London hallmarks for 1900, 21cm. high, 16oz. 15dwt. gross weight without cover.   £4,536

'Three Dahlias', a Lalique blue opalescent circular box and cover of clear and satin finished glass, 20.9cm. diam.   £324

Victorian cut glass and plated biscuit box, on four bun feet.   £55

'Quatre Papillons'. A Lalique frosted glass powder box and cover, the slightly domed top moulded with four moths, 8cm. diam.   £440

GLASS

CANDLESTICKS

Pair of 20th century Colred cut glass candlesticks, European, 14¼in. high. £326

A pair of Tiffany Favrile pastel candle holders, lavender opalescent optic pattern with squared bobeche rim, 3½in. high. £192

A pair of Steuben candlesticks, swirled sticks of clear green with hollow teardrop shaft, 10in. high. £162

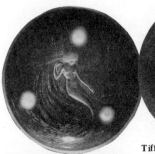

A Tiffany 'Favrile' glass candlestick in iridescent gold, 4½in. high. £180

CHARGERS

A pair of Steuben threaded candlesticks, squat holders of bright Bristol yellow accented with dramatic black threading, 4½in. high. £133

Pair of early 20th century Dominick & Haff sterling silver and cut glass candlesticks, threaded into Classical Revival bases, 13½in. high. £736

'Trepied Sirene', a satin finished and opalescent charger, decorated with a sea sprite, 36.5cm. diam. £2,200

Tiffany decorative rondel, the round flat disc of dark cobalt blue favrile glass with strong blue iridescence,16¼in. diam. £1,085

A large Lalique charger, circular, heavily moulded with three nymphs among vine branches, signed Lalique, France, 40cm. diam. £880

164

DECANTERS

A Venini 'Vetro pesante inciso' decanter and stopper designed by Paolo Venini, circa 1957, 18.5cm. high. £770

A Hukin & Heath 'Crow's foot' decanter, designed by Dr. C. Dresser, electroplate and glass, with registration lozenge for 1879, 24cm. high. £7,776

Early 20th century kew blas decanter, Union Glass Co., Mass, 13½in. high. £163

An Orrefors decanter and stopper, by Nils Landberg. £1,760

An Archimede Seguso 'Compisizione Piume' carafe, circa 1960, 29cm. high. £4,950

A Guild of Handicraft hammered silver and green glass decanter, the design attributed to C. R. Ashbee, with London hallmarks for 1903, 22.5cm. high. £1,296

A Powells 'Whitefriars' glass decanter of green tone, having hammered silver top with ball finial, 26.5cm. high, mark for Hutton & Sons, London 1901. £340

One of a pair of silver mounted cut-glass decanters, each cut-glass body with stellar motifs, by Lorie, maker's mark Cyrillic E. Ch, Moscow, 1899-1908, 12¾in. high, 4490gr. gross. £5,500

A Webb rock crystal decanter and stopper engraved by William Fritsche, the double gourd shaped body engraved in an intaglio technique, circa 1890, 27cm. high. £3,080

GLASS

DISHES

Tiffany glass Floriform dish, gold iridescent bowl form with scalloped and crimped irregular rim, marked 'L.C.T', diam. 4½in.   £97

Lalique amber glass shell duck ashtray, 2¾in. high.   £120

A Lalique glass circular dish, the sides and centre decorated with moulded daisy stems, i 3¼in. wide.   £200

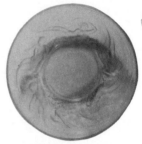

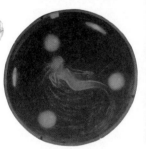

An opalescent 'Ondines' dish, engraved R. Lalique, France, 8in. diam.   £310

One of a pair of Portland clear overshot glass compotes, late 19th century, 8¾in. high.   £335

A Lalique opalescent glass dish, 'Sirene', signed, circa 1925, 14½in. diam.   £650

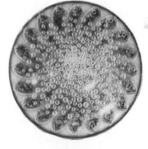

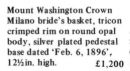

A Lalique opalescent dish, moulded with a radiating pattern of twenty fish and bubbles, with a slightly undulating rim, 35.2cm. diam.   £715

Mount Washington Crown Milano bride's basket, tricon crimped rim on round opal body, silver plated pedestal base dated 'Feb. 6, 1896', 12½in. high.   £1,200

A Lalique opalescent dish, moulded with a radiating pattern of eight carnations and leaves, 35.8cm. diam.   £550

GLASS

Steuben blue Aurene bonbon,
crimped extended rim on
round bowl of cobalt blue,
signed 'Aurene', 6¼in. diam.
£742

A North Country pressed
crystal shaped dish designed
as a basket with cane handle,
circa 1900, 4in. high. £12

An Almaric Walter pate-de-
verre dish of lozenge shape,
designed by H. Berge, 24.6cm.
wide. £1,296

A glass dish attributed to H.
P. Glashutte with enamel
painted decoration of a purple clematis bloom, circa
1900, 23.5cm. diam. £172

A Liberty pewter and Clutha
glass dish on stand, designed
by A. Knox, 6½in. high.
£418

'Ondines', a Lalique opalescent plate, the wide rim moulded with a frieze of water-
nymphs, 27.5cm. diam.
£660

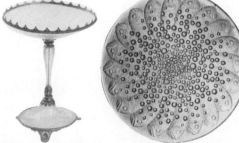

'Anvers', a large Lalique opalescent glass dish, moulded on the
underside with carp amid seaweed, 39.5cm. diam. £2,400

A Viennese gilt metal and engraved glass tazza, encrusted
with turquoise jewelled beads,
possibly Lobmyer, circa 1880,
10½in. high. £1,100

A large Lalique circular, blue
opalescent dish, moulded on
the underside with carp
among bubbles, 35cm. diam.
£825

DRINKING SETS

Bohemian cobalt blue and gilt decorated glass punch set, late 19th century, 15in. high. £571

An Art Deco glass decanter set, the decanter 20.5cm. high and six octagonal glasses, 6.5cm. high. £440

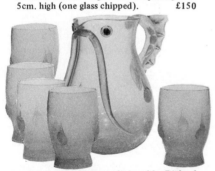

An Art Deco decanter and glasses, the decanter 22.5cm. high and six liqueur glasses 5cm. high (one glass chipped). £150

Two Lalique clear glass decanters and stoppers, the spherical bodies moulded with fine vertical ribbing and twenty glass en suite. £495

A Loetz drinking set, designed by Richard Teschner, comprising a jug and five tumblers, the smokey white glass with polychrome applied decoration, 17.7cm. high. £308

A seventeen piece Lalique drinking set, each piece with moulded motif incorporating two male nudes, with acid-stamped and engraved signatures.. £1,980

GOBLETS

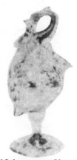

A James Powell flower form goblet, milky vaseline glass, the flower form bowl with frilly rim, 30cm. high. £770

A Wiener Werkstatte enamelled goblet designed by M. von Brunner, the clear glass enamelled in black, blue and red with male and female figures by fruit trees, 15.4cm. high. £550

Late 19th century Venetian goblet vase in nacreous marbled pink and amber, and clear aventurine glass, 12½in. high. £170

A 19th century crystal glass, the hollow bulbous knopped stem containing a Swingewood opal cat and three amethyst mice, circa 1890, 5in. high. £180

A Vienna Secession glass goblet attributed to Moser and the design to J. Hoffmann, circa 1915, 12.8cm. high. £270

One of a set of six Tiffany 'Favrile' champagne coupes, 15cm. high. £1,650

A Wiener Werkstatte glass goblet, the design attributed to Dagobert Peche, 8.4cm. high. £220

One of a pair of champagne coupes, by Hans Christiansen, 17cm. high. £1,100

An Almeric Walter pate-de-verre goblet, designed by Henri Berge, 6¼in. high. £900

JUGS

A cut glass tapering claret jug with domed hinged cover, 8¾in. high.   £99

A Gunderson Burmese pitcher, of delicate Burmese pink to pastel yellow colouring, 13in. high.   £59

Smith Bros. enamel decorated creamer, Mass., circa 1890, 3.3/8in. high.   £104

A Galle oviform single-handled ewer, the silver mount modelled with stylised flowers, signed, 10¼in. high.   £820

An enamelled glass jug with stopper, by Galle, decorated with enamelled hearts and a dwarf playing a violin, 20cm. high.   £440

A Continental silver mounted ewer, the silver cap with embossed fruit decoration, on a lead crystal base, 10in. high.   £95

Glossy Burmese moulded cream pitcher, Boston & Sandwich Glass Co., 1885, 3¼in. high.   £244

An oviform water jug with applied scroll handle, 6½in. high.   £33

Crown Milano enamel decorated cream pitcher, Mt. Washington Glass Co., circa 1893, 4¼in. high.   £314

JUGS

A Victorian silver mounted dimple glass claret jug, London, 1894, 6¾in. high. £187

An amberina syrup pitcher with silverplated undertray, New England Glass Company, 5½in. high. £281

Wheeling peach blow drape pattern pitcher, Hobbs, Brockunier & Co., circa 1886, 4½in. high. £212

Threaded art glass pitcher, tinted in cranberry and amber, circa 1890, 8½in. high. £157

A Galle enamelled and green oviform single-handled glass jug, 8½in. high, inscribed. £200

A hand cut crystal tall pitcher with notched handle, circa 1890. £171

A diamond quilted satin glass creamer, probably England, circa 1880, 3¾in. high. £174

A Dutch silver and cut glass flagon, circa 1900, with rococo reserves, scrolls and busts on a stippled ground, 14in high. £1,005

An amberina miniature cream pitcher, New England Glass Co., Mass., circa 1880, 2½in. high. £157

An ovoid glass claret jug with a star design, the plain mount with bracket handle, 7¾in. high. £88

A Moser oviform jug, with amber tinted handle and tricorn rim, the body graduating from red to amber and decorated in raised enamels. £1,210

Late Victorian cut glass claret jug, by John Round, Sheffield, 1898, 10in. high. £440

A Victorian electroplated claret jug, by Elkington & Co., with date letter code for 1883, 36cm. high. £242

A large Schneider mottled glass pitcher, in red glass streaked with yellow, 1920's. £250

D. Christian cameo glass pitcher, shaped upright pouring lip and applied handle on slender cylindrical form, signature 'D. Christian/Meisenthal/Loth', height 10¼in. £782

A Hukin & Heath EPNS mounted large cut glass claret jug, 12in. high. £190

An Elton jug with bifurcated spout and handle above, 18cm. high. £270

An engraved claret jug with plated mounts and hinged cover, circa 1880, 27.5cm. high. £259

LAMPSHADES

'Acanthus', a Lalique frosted glass hanging shade heavily moulded with stepped feather-like pattern, 17¾in. diam. £880

Two Quezal gas light shades, both of opal glass in squat bulbed form, 5in. diam. £171

A Galle carved and acid etched double overlay plafonnier, of shaped circular form, overlaid with a green ground and dark amber marguerites, 34.2cm. diam. £4,620

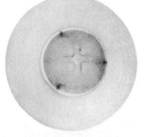

A large Daum cameo glass hanging lampshade of shallow domed form, 46cm. diam., signed. £2,100

'Dahlia', a Lalique opalescent and frosted hanging shade moulded with large flower heads, 12in. diam. £770

A 1930's plafonnier, the half-round blue tinted bowl moulded with coquilles, signed R. Lalique, France, 17½in. full diam. £220

A Daum hanging shade, the milky and frosted acid treated ground overlaid with acid cut decoration of coral coloured berries and leaves. £2,200

A Burmese art glass lamp shade, with black "etched" scene of birds, insects, dragonflies, crickets and bees, 5¾in. high. £207

A Sabino glass hanging shade the clear glass moulded with an interlocking circular motif and a frieze of stylised roses in high relief, 46.2cm. diam. £374

MISCELLANEOUS

A rare Webb cameo glass framed clock, the shield shaped frame of yellow overlaid opal white, Birmingham, England, 7in. high. £2,071

A Mount Washington/Pairpoint cracker jar, decorated in the Crown Milano manner with blossoms and leaves, 6½in. high. £266

A large Galle carved and acid etched double overlay hanging light, globular form overlaid with green and dark amber pendant clematis, 35.2cm. high. £7,700

'Source de la Fontaine', a Lalique statue, the clear and satin-finished glass moulded as a standing maiden holding a fish in front of her, 54cm. high without base. £4,950

A pair of Nancy pate de verre bookends fashioned as dolphins, signed X Momillon, 6½in. high. £2,500

An Art Deco glass cocktail shaker with silver mounts, Birmingham, 1936, 8in. high. £400

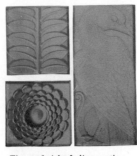

An Etling opalescent figure of a semi naked woman, 11in. high. £480

Three of eight Lalique satin glass panels, three rectangular and five of square shape, one panel signed R. Lalique. £1,100

'Cote d'Azur Pullman Express', a Lalique figure, the clear satin finished glass moulded as a naked maiden, 16.8cm. high. £3,080

MISCELLANEOUS

A Loetz type art glass covered jar, of clear simulated crackle glass decorated with four applied prunts of emerald green, 7¼in. high. £44

A Lalique glass inkwell. £1,125

Early 20th century dimpled glass firescreen with an oak frame. £38

A Pairpoint art glass pickle jar and holder, cranberry coloured jar decorated with enamelled aster blossoms, 13in. high. £133

An Edwardian electro plated tantalus, with three square section decanters and stoppers and the original keys, by Daniel and Arter of Birmingham, 42.7cm. across. £550

"La Donna Somersa" art glass sculpture, by Da Rossi of Murano, Italy, with gold leaf wrapped figure, 16½in. high. £828

A Lalique clear and frosted glass presse-papier, the plaque intaglio moulded with the figure of St. Christopher carrying the infant Christ. 4½in. high. £440

A Lalique frosted swan figure, with head erect in swimming position, signed "Lalique/France" on base, 9¾in. high. £887

'Suzanne', a Lalique opalescent glass statuette of a naked maiden, her arms outstretched and holding her robes, 22.6cm. high. £8,800

SCENT BOTTLES

A rare Webb gem cameo perfume bottle, designed and executed by George Woodall, of opaque opal white overlaid with coral, 4½in. high. £3,254

A Galle carved and acid etched cameo scent bottle, the clear and pale green glass overlaid with red fruit blossom, 11.5cm. high. £600

'A Cotes Bouchon Papillon', a Lalique amber stained scent bottle and stopper, 6.5cm. high. £440

A Galle enamelled glass perfume bottle and stopper, enamelled in colours with a butterfly hovering above delicate flowers, 16cm. high. £1,400

Galle cameo glass perfume bottle and mushroom stopper, 4½in. wide, 3¾in. high. £440

An unusual Lalique frosted glass atomiser modelled in high relief with two birds nesting together, 9.5cm. wide. £460

'Quatre Soleils', a Lalique frosted glass scent bottle and stopper, of almost conical shape moulded with linear decoration, 7.2cm. high. £7,000

'Panier de Roses'. A Lalique frosted glass scent bottle, moulded with basket work enclosing rosebuds spilling over the top, 10cm. high. £1,700

An 18th century English clear glass scent bottle of flattened pear shape with gold cagework mount in the manner of James Cox, circa 1775. £720

SCENT BOTTLES

A Webb gem cameo perfume bottle, of bright blue layered in white, cameo cut and carved overall with a wide band of five-petalled blossoms, 4½in. high.   £1,065

A Lalique scent bottle and stopper, each face moulded with a flowerhead heightened with brown staining, 5.7cm. high.   £1,000

A Webb gem cameo perfume/ cologne bottle, of luminous red overlaid opal white, fitted with original glass stopper, 5in. high.   £710

A rare Lalique glass perfume bottle, the stopper moulded as the full figure of a maiden wearing a long dress studded with flowers, 10cm. high.
£1,100

A very attractive Victorian Scottish scent bottle of horse-shoe shape, set with panels of different coloured agates, unmarked, circa 1880.   £300

A Galle enamelled glass perfume bottle and stopper, enamelled with an insect amid foliate branches, 15cm. high.   £750

'Flacon Deux Fleurs', a Lalique frosted glass scent bottle, formed as two overlapping flowerheads with beaded centers, 9cm high.
£270

A Lalique black glass scent bottle and stopper made for Ambrl D'Orsay, moulded in each corner with a woman in long dress holding a garland, 5in. high.   £1,430

A Galle scent bottle, with enamel painted decoration of a landscape, seaweed and seashell decoration, 11cm. high.   £935

STAINED GLASS

A large 19th century English stained glass panel showing a lady in Renaissance costume at the prie-dieu, 100 x 55cm.
£495

An Art Deco leaded stained glass panel by Jacques Gruber, 70.2cm. wide, 50.3cm. high. £3,520

A large rectangular glass panel by John Hutton, sand blasted and wheel engraved with Perseus before the Three Graces, 206.5 x 97cm. £1,650

One of two early 20th century prairie school-style leaded glass windows, 20½ x 53½in., and five smaller, 18 x 18¾in. £769

A 19th century Chinese painting on glass with a group of richly clad children playing with flowers, one with a model goldfish, 28½in. wide. £648

A large 19th century English stained glass panel of Mary Queen of Scots, 151 x 80cm.
£1,100

A leaded and stained glass panel by George Walton, after a design by Charles Rennie Mackintosh, 133.6cm. high, 91.4cm. wide.
£660

A circular stained glass panel, by W. Aikman, depicting a rural landscape with a ploughman and horses in the foreground, 1924, 45cm. diam.
£200

A late 19th century leaded stained and coloured glass window, signed W. J. McPherson, Tremont St., Boston, Mass. £490

STAINED GLASS

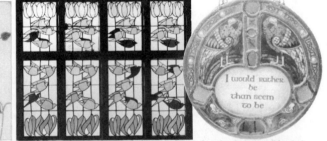

A stained glass window, the design attributed to E. A. Taylor, of a blue bird amidst stylised curvilinear pink blooms, above a field of bluebells, 81 x109.5cm.
£550

Leaded glass window with central portrait of a young woman with colourful flowers and a bird at each side, 50in. long.
£685

A circular stained glass panel, painted with the head and shoulders of a young girl, circa 1880, 26.8cm.
£100

One of a pair of stained glass windows, the design attributed to E. A. Taylor, each with a blue bird amidst stylised curvilinear pink blooms, 82 x 56.4cm.
£715

A lead and stained glass window designed by M. H. Baillie-Scott consisting of four large and four small rectangular panels, in green, blue and puce-coloured glass, (1897-1898).
£14,300

A stained glass and leaded roundel by Jessie Jacobs, painted with two birds above a kidney shaped pane inscribed 'I would Rather be than seem to be', 24.3cm. diam.
£200

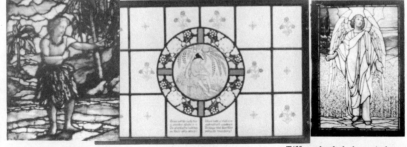

John LaFarge leaded glass panel, of 'stained', painted and layered segments of textured mottled and multi-coloured glass, 16½ x 13¼in.
£7,428

A stained glass window, depicting a shepherd with crook and pipe sitting beneath a tree, 56cm. x 85cm.
£450

Tiffany leaded glass window, full figure portrait of an angel with a field of spring flowers and intricately designed landscape beyond, 34 x 29in.
£8,000

VASES

A Venini patchwork vase designed by Fulvio Bianconi, decorated in patches of blue, red, green and clear glass, 19cm. high. £3,520

A Galle double overlay mould-blown oviform vase, etched with gherkins and large leaves, 7¼in. high. £1,980

A Loetz two handled vase, the iridescent green glass overlaid with a silvery-blue oil splashed pattern, 14.5cm. high. £286

'Archers', a Lalique cased butterscotch glass vase, moulded in shallow relief with a group of naked archers, 25.5cm. high. £3,400

A Barovier and Toso two handled vase, the clear glass internally decorated with violet 'latticino' pattern and gold-foil, 29.8cm. high. £220

A Galle carved and acid etched double overlay vase, the pale amber glass overlaid with royal blue and dark green harebells, 21cm. high. £2,090

'Claritas', an Iittala glass vase, designed by Timo Sarpaneva, the thick clear glass internally decorated in black with white roundels, 26cm. high. £330

'Aras'. A Lalique emerald-green glass vase, moulded with parakeets amid dense foliage laden with berries, 23cm. high. £6,800

A Daum acid textured and carved double overlay vase of flaring shouldered form with two small handles at the neck, 24.5cm. high. £14,300

VASES

A Loetz vase of swollen gadrooned ovoid form with flaring neck, the amethyst coloured glass painted with a blue, green and silver network, 18cm. high. £605

A Loetz white metal mounted vase, decorated with cobalt-blue trailed and silvery-green oil splashed patterns on an iridescent peach ground, 20.5cm. high. £2,860

'Milan', a Lalique brown stained vase, the clear and satin finished glass moulded with stylised leafy branches, 28.4cm. high. £1,430

A Loetz gourd shaped vase of triangular section, with an elaborate combed and trailed iridescent silvery-blue and orange pattern on pale amber ground, 26.6cm. high. £5,500

A large Sam Herman pumpkin form vase, the slightly opaque glass internally decorated with a blue and yellow asymmetrical pattern, 28.2cm. high. £660

A Loetz vase, the design attributed to Dagobert Peche, the lemon-yellow body on a deep purple base decorated with a blue iridescent splashed pattern, 19.8cm. high. £495

'Bleuets', a Lalique glass vase of bucket form, intaglio moulded on the exterior with cornflowers, 15.6cm. high. £380

A cased glass vase designed by Michael Powolny, bell shaped on knopped circular foot, 19.2cm. high. £220

'Aigrettes', a Lalique smoky-grey glass vase, crisply moulded on the exterior with exotic birds in flight, 25cm. high. £3,200

VASES

'Marisa', a Lalique vase, the milky-white glass moulded with four graduated bands of fish, (minute rim chip), 22.7cm. high. £2,640

'Avallon', a Lalique opalescent glass vase, heavily moulded with birds perched amongst fruit-bearing cherry branches (rim chip), 15.8cm. high. £440

A Loetz vase of swollen dimpled form with everted rim, the yellow glass with a blue-green iridescent trailed design, 10.7cm. high. £880

A Leerdam enamelled vase, designed by Andreas Dirk Copier, the pale red glass with black enamel decoration, 27.8cm. high. £572

A Barovier and Toso patchwork vase designed by Ercole Barovier, the clear glass internally decorated with graduated rectangles inside each other, circa 1955, 14.5cm. high. £550

A Lamartine acid textured and enamelled vase, the clear glass internally decorated with blue-white flecks and polychrome enamelled with an extensive wooded landscape, 13.4cm. high. £330

A Val St Lambert vase, the 'soapstone' ground overlaid with streaked crimson and green glass, 18cm. high. £330

A Loetz footed vase, the swollen body with applied arch decoration, with iridescent purple and golden-green decoration, 24.3cm. high. £550

A Daum Art Deco vase, the auburn tinted clear glass decorated with a pattern of ribs, 26.3cm. high. £495

182

VASES

A Muller Freres carved and acid textured cameo vase, the mottled orange, yellow and brown cased glass overlaid with a green fruiting vine, 12.5cm. high. £572

A small Galle carved and acid etched triple overlay vase, the light pink glass cased in clear glass and overlaid with white, blue and green umbel flowers, 8.5cm high. £396

A Lalique brown stained vase, of flared form, moulded with relief decoration of birds amid foliage, 22.7cm. high. £495

A Daum vase, with acid cut decoration of coral coloured berries and leaves, 17.5cm. high. £1,650

A Galle vase, the opaque jade green glass overlaid with sang de boeuf, with carved and acid etched decoration of a tiger lily, 22cm. high. £5,500

A Loetz vase, with two lug handles, internally decorated with tiny air bubbles and cased in blue glass, 23.3cm.high. £330

A Daum vase, the sombre pink ground overlaid with amethyst, with carved and acid etched decoration of bats, 26cm. high. £2,420

'Formose', a Lalique blue stained vase, molded with a shoal of goldfish, with moulded signature R. Lalique, 17.5cm. high. £825

A Lalique brown stained vase, of flared form, moulded with relief decoration of birds amid foliage, 22.7cm. high. £1,045

A Prussian M.1915 Ersatz (Pressed Felt) O.R's Pickel-haube of a Pioneer Battalion. £140

A very rare helmet of an experimental pattern for French Dragoon regiments circa 1900, bearing manu-facturer's stamp: B. Franck et ses fils, Aubervilliers. £400

Officer's helmet of The King's Own Norfolk Imperial Yeomanry, circa 1915. £775

A Bavarian M.1915 Uhlan ORs Tschapska, grey painted helmet plate and mounts. £180

A very good post-1902 officer's blue cloth spiked helmet of The North Staffordshire Regiment, gilt mounts, velvet backed chinchain. £470

A Hesse M. 1915 Infantry-man's Pickelhaube, grey paint-ed helmet plate and mounts leather lining and chinstrap. £150

A Bavarian M.1915 Dragoon O.Rs Pickelhaube, grey paint-ed helmet plate and mounts. £120

A post-1902 officer's shako of The Highland Light Infantry. £210

Trooper's helmet of The King's Own Norfolk Imperial Yeomanry, circa 1910. £350

A rare 'The Pocket Typewriter, Swan Arcade, Bradford', with name and characters on circular white enamel dial, 10cm. long, circa 1887. £1,100

A Melloni's thermopile by Griffin & Tatlock Ltd., with telescopic stand and the associated tangent galvanometer, 9in. high. £99

A ship's magnetic detector by Marconi's Wireless Telegraph Co., No. 71335, in polished teak case. £4,620

A late 19th century oxidised and lacquered brass simple theodolite, signed on the plate R. W. Street & Co., in mahogany case, 15¾in. wide £352

A Jean Schoenner, Nurnberg, toy spherical magic lantern with polished metal body and black painted support. £132

F. E. Ives/The Photochromo-scope Syndicate Ltd., London, Kromskop viewer with viewing hood and diffusing screen. £825

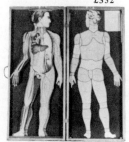

Anatomical teaching device, 'Smiths's New Outline Map of the Human System, Anatomical Regions, No. 2', manufactured by American Manikan Co., Peoria, Illinois, 1888, 44in. high. £514

A 19th century French pewter enema douche with accessories in fitted oval japanned case, 8in. wide. £264

A 200 x 140mm. Polyrama Panoptique viewer with focusing lens section, opening lid and label 'Polyrama Panoptique, Brevet d'Invention SGtie du Govt'. £880

A cast iron funeral gate by James Monahan, Savannah, Georgia, late 19th century, centering a reticulated weeping willow tree, 33 x 27¾in. £714

A 20th century, white painted wrought iron gazebo, worked with tubular members in the form of a painted arch, 120in. wide. £2,457

A Gordon Russell polished steel set of fire irons, the stand with square section column, arched legs and trefoil feet. £880

One of a pair of French enamelled cast iron urns, decorated with geometric foliage and flowerheads on a cream ground, late 19th century, 15in. high. £3,080

A pair of cast iron figural andirons, America, late 19th/early 20th century, caricature figures of a black man and woman, 16½in. high. £581

Cast iron State Seal of New York, America, late 19th century, the figure of an eagle with outstretched wings perched upon a scrolled cartouche, 34in. wide. £1,257

Victorian polished steel coal scuttle with a lifting flap and shovel. £90

A brass mounted steel basket grate with arched rectangular cast iron back, late 19th century, 34½in. wide. £1,980

A cast iron architectural ornament, American, early 20th century, modelled in the form of a Classical head, 22in. high. £454

Late 19th century American cast iron elk figure, 49in. wide. £1,959

Early 20th century Art Deco cast and wrought iron parcel gilt pier table, France, 53in. wide. £659

A wrought iron snake sculpture by Edgar Brandt, of a king cobra coiled in a circle with its head raised to strike, dark patina, stamped E. Brandt, 11.5cm. high. £660

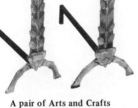

A moulded zinc polychrome tobacconist figure, Wm. Demuth, N.Y., circa 1890, 67½in. high without base. £6,875

A pair of Arts and Crafts polished steel firedogs, designed by Ernest Gimson and made by Alfred Bucknell, 58.5cm. high. £1,750

A cast iron panel by Hector Guimard for the entrance to the Paris Metro, 74cm. high. £1,100

A cast iron tea kettle, the sides cast in low relief with numerous chrysanthemum blooms, 5¼in. diam. £99

A cast iron painted mill weight, American, late 19th/early 20th century, modelled as a bob-tailed standing horse, 16½in. high. £259

One of a pair of iron Komai baluster vases decorated in two shades of gilt, signed Moriyama, circa 1890, 13.7cm. high. £885

IVORY

Late 19th century carved sectional ivory okimono of a street vendor, signed Munehisa, 15.8cm. high.
£385

An ivory mounted casket with domed hinged cover, the protruding base on bun feet, late 19th century, 13in. wide. £770

A late 19th century French ivory figurine of Cupid ensnared, possibly after a model by L.Samain, 10cm. high.
£253

Late 19th century boxwood, rootwood and ivory group of doves attending their young, signed Mitsuhiro, 49cm. high.
£11,000

Early 20th century Japanese ivory boat, hull with veneered carved and stained rectangular panels, 15¼in. high, on shaped wooden base.
£514

An ivory and silver vase, the lobed ivory body decorated with cockerels and hens and their chicks among a bamboo grove, the silver mounts decorated in various coloured cloisonne enamels, signed Hidetomo, late 19th century, 20cm. high.
£1,760

A well carved ivory okimono of an elegantly dressed lady holding a scarf, signed Kazusane, late 19th century, 15cm. high.
£1,100

An Art Deco ivory bust of a nude maiden, her head turned sideways, on a flaring shaped ebony plinth, 24.3cm. high.
£1,100

A fine ivory tusk vase and cover carved in high relief with a multitude of quail among millet, late 19th century, 25.2cm. high.
£4,290

IVORY

A fine ivory group of a man holding one of his sons in his arms, another kneeling beside a basket of peaches, signed Seiga, late 19th century, 15cm. high.   £1,650

A fine ivory and lacquer figure of a seated Tea Master, his kimono decorated in gold and silver hiramakie on a Kinji ground, signed Komin, late 19th century, 15.7cm. high.   £4,950

A finely carved ivory figure of an old man feeding grain to a hen and two chicks at his feet, signed Seirin, late 19th century, 15cm. high.   £1,430

Late 19th century carved sectional ivory okimono of a man and a small boy, signed Munehisa, 15.5cm. high.
£935

A well carved ivory group of a cockerel, hen and three chicks on wood stand, late 19th century, overall 18cm. wide. £1,100

Late 19th century ivory carving of an itinerant basket seller, signed Hododa, 35.3cm. high.
£2,420

Late 19th century ivory vase and cover inlaid in shibayama style, signed Gyokiukendo san, 20cm. high.   £3,300

A 19th century ball, stained and carved in relief with rats among tassles and objects, 2½in. diam.   £231

An early 20th century English ivory bust of Mrs. Emmeline Pankhurst, by A.G.Walker, signed on the back, on a grey marble pedestal, 16.5cm. high.   £2,750

A Lalique gilt metal mounted glass brooch, moulded with two birds of prey flanking a cabochon, 9.5cm. long. £1,000

A sapphire and diamond triple cluster bar brooch, with three oval cut sapphires within a surround of a total of twenty-six small old cut diamonds. £1,430

A stylish Georg Jensen silver bracelet designed by Henning Koppel, formed by six heavily wrought amoebic like links, 21cm. long, 1957. £480

A pate de verre pendant, the mottled yellow and amber glass decorated in high relief with a red and green beetle. 4.6cm. diam. £605

A 19th century sapphire and diamond frog brooch, set in silver and gold. £3,400

A Victorian pietra-dura and gold brooch, with a mosaic flower spray in colours. £462

A diamond monogram pendant, the centre with diamond chip EFS monogram. £198

A diamond stylised flower spray brooch, set throughout with various brilliant and baguette cut stones. £3,850

A lapis, coral and gold brooch by Cartier in the form of a stylised scarab beetle, the head a cabochon coral. £1,650

A very attractive diamond set, yellow coloured gold bracelet, signed Cartier, circa 1950. £4,100

A diamond, ruby and sapphire butterfly brooch, the diamond chip wings capped with rubies and sapphires. £748

An Edwardian diamond and enamel panel brooch, of oblong shape with canted corners, one stone deficient. £2,100

190

A diamond, half pearl and ruby brooch in the form of a lizard, in a fitted case from Elkington and Co. Ltd., 73 Cheapside, E.C.
£1,265

A diamond and pearl bangle, with a single pearl within a surround of twelve old cut diamonds, from Dobson and Sons, 32 Piccadilly, London, dated 1884.
£1,705

A plique-a-jour pin with fresh-water pearls, probably French, circa 1910, marked 800, 1½in. long.
£119

A pearl and diamond roun-del brooch, the central pearl within a surround of nine small old cut diamonds.
£1,155

A Victorian turquoise and gold buckle brooch, in the form of a scroll with central buckle.
£572

A Kerr gilded Art Nouveau brooch, 6.5cm. across, stamped with maker's mark, Sterling and 1702.
£300

A late Victorian diamond star brooch, with a central cluster of a brilliant collet within a sur-round of eight similar smaller diamonds.
£1,760

A Lalique brooch, the clear and satin finished glass moulded with marguerites, on rose pink foil ground.
£1,650

A rare enamelled Lalique glass ring, of blue colour with domed cabochon top, 2.5cm. wide.
£1,700

A Tiffany & Co. two-colour gold, sapphire and moonstone oval brooch, 3.3cm. across.
£700

A white metal and plique a jour scarab brooch, the green gem scarab with wings enamelled in shades of green and pink, set with a ruby.
£550

Art Deco diamond bow pin, pave-set with 105 diamonds weighing approx. 3.00ct. and highlighted by calibre cut onyx.
£2,500

LAMPS

A Murano panelled glass oil lamp, with caramel and green slag glass panels, 1905, 19in. high. £473

A Steuben table lamp, classic form of lustrous blue Aurene mounted in Art Deco fittings, vase 11in. high. £414

A mica and hammered copper table lamp, possibly Benedict Studios, New York, early 20th century, 19in. diam. £1,428

A Moe Bridges parrot lamp, with reverse handpainted scene of two exotic birds centred in a summer landscape, 23in. high. £2,721

A Tiffany bronze table lamp with lotus shade, of Oriental umbrella form with brilliant blue rectangular glass segments, 26in. high. £18,934

A Pairpoint scenic table lamp, handpainted with four nautical scenes of tall ships separated by seashell panels, 23in. high. £1,538

A Tiffany bronze lamp with spider and web shade, of mottled muted grey-green coloured rectangular panels divided into six segments, 19in. high. £10,650

A leaded slag glass and oak table lamp, early 20th century, the square hipped shade with coloured glass panels, 22in. high. £742

An art glass table lamp, open Tam o' Shanter shade of green iridescent pulled and swirled damascene design cased to opal-white glass, 19½in. high. £1,005

192

LAMPS

A mica and hammered copper table lamp, possibly Benedict Studios, New York, early 20th century, unsigned, 16in. high. £685

A Handel scenic table lamp, handpainted on the interior with a scenic landscape of summer birches and poplar trees, 23in. high. £1,538

A Handel leaded glass lamp shade with Hampshire Pottery base, early 20th century, signed, 1851, 21in. high. £2,142

A Tiffany Studios table lamp, on four-pronged spider ring attached to matching insert, 17in. high. £1,183

An art glass table lamp, with gilt metal fittings supporting two glass shades of opal and gold, 28in. high. £295

A Handel parrot lamp, hand-painted with three brilliantly coloured parrots, against a flower strewn background, 24in. high. £13,017

A Tiffany leaded glass lamp shade on Grueby pottery base, early 20th century, with dome shaped shade in acorn pattern, artist initialled A. L. for Annie Lingley, 17¾in. high. £11,428

A desk lamp with Steuben Aurene shade, bronzed metal standard, mirror lustre at top, 13½in. high. £325

A Fulper pottery and leaded glass table lamp, New Jersey, signed Vasekraft, stamped "Patents pending in United States and Canada, England, France and Germany", 20½in. high. £6,285

A table top mirror on shoe foot base, by Gustav Stickley, circa 1910, 21¼in. high. £432

An Art Nouveau electroplated mirror and stand, the cartouche form decorated with two maidens with trumpets amid scrolling foliage, 42.8cm. long. £308

Shop-O'-The Crafters mahogany wall mirror, Ohio, 1910, 27½in. high, 30½in. wide. £468

A WMF Secessionist electroplated mirror, 34cm. high. £825

A giltwood mirror with bevelled rectangular plate, the frame crisply carved with ribbon-tied berried foliage, late 19th century, 59 x 49½in. £660

A WMF electroplated pewter mirror, stamped marks B 2/0 GK H, 40cm. high. £462

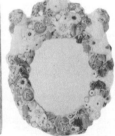

A Carlo Bugatti ebonized and vellum covered mirror, the rectangular plate with circular top, 177.5cm. high; 90cm. wide. £1,210

An Arts and Crafts pewter and mother-of-pearl wall mirror, decorated with rectangular panels inlaid in mother-of-pearl, 60.3 x 87cm. £850

A Wiener Keramik oval mirror, designed by Michael Powolny, formed as a multi-coloured floral garland surmounted at the top with a yellow sparrow, 29.5cm. long. £280

The L.M.S. Class 5XP 4-6-0 locomotive and tender No. 5500 'Patriot' built by P. Hammond and painted by L. Richards, 3¾ x 17½in. £1,210

A rare Marklin electric model of the G.W.R. 4-6-2 'Pacific' locomotive and bogie tender, circa 1909. £3,850

5in. gauge live steam 0-6-0 tank locomotive in British Rail black livery No. 1505. £850

A Hornby (3-rail) electric model of the LMS 4-6-2 locomotive and tender No. 6201 "Princess Elizabeth", in original paintwork, circa 1937. £990

A Hornby clockwork L.M.S. 'No. 1 Tank Good Set', comprising an 0-4-0 tank locomotive, a 'Shell Motor Spirit', an open wagon, a brake van and a circle of track, in original box, circa 1926. £209

Wells clockwork 'Mickey Mouse Circus Train', comprising an 0-4 0 A4 locomotive No. 2509 'Silver Link', a tender with Mickey Mouse and a lithographed 'Circus Dining Car', circa 1948, £880

A well detailed two-rail electric model of the G.W.R. 48XX Class 0 4-2 side tank locomotive No. 4837 and auto coach No. 187 built by B. Miller, 3¼ x 25¾in. £5,500

A rare Marklin Jubilee Set No. AR12930/35/3, comprising a 'Planet' locomotive and tender, a stage type coach and an open carriage, all in original paintwork, circa 1935. £3,850

MONEY BANKS

Cast iron money bank, 'The lion and two monkeys', 23cm. high. £130

A 20th century English cast iron 'Dinah' mechanical bank, by John Harper & Co. Ltd., 6½in. high. £125

"I Always Did 'Spise a Mule", a cast iron mechanical bank of a negro jockey riding a mule, probably by J. Harper and Co., circa 1910, 10½in. long. £308

'Bull Dog Bank' cast iron mechanical bank, J. & E. Stevens, Co., pat. 1880, 7½in. high. £347

A William Tell cast iron money bank, 1896, the figure firing coins placed on his crossbow into a slot above a boy's head, 10½in. £220

Owl cast iron mechanical bank, by J. & E. Stevens Co., pat. 1880, 7.5/8in. high. £150

'World's Fair' cast iron mechanical bank, J. & E. Stevens, Co., pat. 1893, 8¼in. long. £450

Late 19th century American 'Uncle Sam' mechanical bank, by Shepard Hardware Co., 11½in. high. £250

American cast iron money bank, 'Hall's Lilliput Bank'. £280

196

MUSICAL BOXES

A New Melba gramophone by the Gramophone & Typewriter Limited, with triple spring worm drive motor, 1907-8. £1,210

A bells-in-sight musical box with 14in. cylinder and six bells playing ten airs and with original air sheet, two-part comb lacks one tooth. £1,600

An Edison Fireside phonograph, Model A No. 25426, the K reproducer, crane and 36 two-minute and four-minute wax cylinders in cartons. £462

A Harmonia 16¼in. disc musical box with single comb movement and walnut veneered case, 23in. wide, with ten discs. £1,100

A Columbia Regal/Sterling disc graphophone in panelled oak case with engaged corner columns, aluminium tone-arm and nickel plated flower horn, circa 1907. £770

A 19.5/8in. upright Polyphon with coin mechanism and drawer, in glazed walnut case, 38in. high. £3,850

An Edison Bell Electron Model 248 cabinet gramophone with Edison Bell Electron soundbox on S-shaped tone-arm, 35½in. high. £605

A Celestina twenty-note organette in gilt stencilled walnut case, with fourteen rolls and nineteen new rolls. £825

A gramophone in the form of a miniature grand piano with Thorens soundbox, in mahogany case on paired tapered legs, 54in. long. £605

NETSUKE

Hozan (late 19th century), Mask of Okina, netsuke, boxwood, 4.2cm. high, signed Hokkyo Hozan. £932

Morita Soko (1879-1942), A crate of tangerines, netsuke, boxwood with dark wood inlay, 4cm. high, signed Soko. £12,429

Hirado Kilns (late 19th century), Mouse, netsuke, white glazed porcelain with black enamel details, 5.5cm. long, unsigned. £683

Anonymous (20th century), A humanoid kirin, netsuke, wood, 6.5cm. high, unsigned. £497

Ouchi Sosui (1907/11-72), Lady Tokiwa Gozen with her children fleeing through the snow, netsuke, ivory, 5cm. high, signed Sosui to, in inscribed wood box signed Sosui koku. £4,350

Anonymous (19th century), Cranes in flight, netsuke, natural gourd with lacquer decoration, silver fittings, 6cm. high, unsigned. £1,180

A finely carved ivory netsuke of an ama and a kappa embracing, signed Akihide (born 1934), 6.2cm. high. £1,320

A wood netsuke, carved as a skeleton kneeling beating a large mokugyo, ivory hole rims, signed. £220

A well carved lightly stained ivory netsuke of a standing baku looking up, signed Kangyoku (born 1944), 4.8cm. £825

PEWTER

A W. M. F. electroplated pewter tray, with pierced and raised decoration of an Art Nouveau maiden with flowing hair and an iris, 33.1cm. diam. £209

One of a pair of Art Nouveau pewter three light candelabra, each with flowerhead sconces with foliate drip-pans, 25.5cm. high. £580

A Liberty & Co. 'Tudric' pewter box and cover, designed by Archibald Knox, 11.9cm. high. £264

A Palme Konig und Habel vase mounted in a pewter stand, with pierced mount formed by three Art Nouveau maidens on pierced tripartite stand, 24.3cm. high. £528

A Liberty and Co. pewter four piece tea service designed by Archibald Knox, the teapot with compressed globular body, stamped Made in England, English Pewter. £495

A Liberty & Co. 'Tudric' pewter timepiece, showing the influences of C.F.A. Voysey, in the form of a dwelling, 34cm. high. £1,850

German pewter three-handled soup tureen with boar mount, by Kayserzinn, 15in. high. £250

One of a pair of W. M. F. electroplated pewter candelabra, each modelled as a scantily clad Art Nouveau maiden, with usual W. M. F. marks, 26.5cm. high. £1,100

A WMF pewter coupe, the pierced oval body formed by two Art Nouveau butterfly-maidens, with shaped green glass liner, 17.8cm. high. £308

PHOTOGRAPHS

F.E. Currey, Iris and chrysanthemum, two platinum prints, 7½ x 5½in. and 8 x 6in., unmounted (1880s or early 90s). £198

'Miners returning to daylight, South Wales', by B. Brandt, gelatin silver print, 16 x 12in., 1930's. £450

Yousuf Karsh, Ernest Hemingway, gelatin silver print, 12 x 10in., titled and credited, 1957. £143

Francis Bruguiere — New York Theatre Studies — Eight gelatin silver prints, approx. 8¾ x 10in. to 10¼ x 12½in. 1920/30's. £550

1887: A photograph of Queen Victoria, seated, signed bottom right 'Victoria...1887', framed and glazed. £700

Govt. Printer, N.S.W. — New South Wales 1911 — One of sixty-eight gelatin silver prints, each approx. 11 x 14in. £880

Margaret Bourke-White — In a Korean village, a wife, mother and grandmother lament the death of their boy — Gelatin silver print, 10¾ x 14¼in., early 1940's. £462

Baron Adolf de Meyer — Still life with parasols, hat stands and flowers — Gelatin silver print, 7 x 9 in., after 1914. £220

Mr Mendenhall — Photos of San Franciso Earthquake taken for Government Record by Mr Mendenhall of the Geodetic Survey 1906 — Forty-one gelatin silver prints, 1906. £825

PHOTOGRAPHS

A Dexo Hoffman black and white gelatin silver print of Marilyn Monroe and Sir Lawrence Olivier, 1958. £250

Captain Scott and the Polar Expedition, album containing thirty-nine gelatin silver prints, various sizes, 1901. £418

Angus McBean, 'Toumanova 'surrealized' as La Sylphide', gelatin silver print, 19¼ x 14¾in., signature and date 'London '38' in pencil on card. £143

Bill Brandt, Parlormaid and under-parlormaid ready to serve dinner, gelatin silver print, 35¼ x 30in., with photographer's ink stamp and initials 'B.B.' on reverse, 1930s. £1,045

A signed portrait photograph by D.Wilding of King George VI, Queen Elizabeth, Princess Elizabeth and Princess Margaret in Coronation robes, dated 1937, 20cm. x 28cm. £520

Sacha Stone — Lady painting numbers — Gelatin silver print, 6¾ x 8½in., early 1920's. £385

Eadweard Muybridge — Animal Locomotion: men — Eleven photogravure prints, approx. image sizes 9½ x 12¼, 1887. £440

J. Frish — London river scenes — Five gelatin prints, image size approx. 8 x 12in., 1940's. £121

Heinz Loew — Corsets — Three gelatin silver prints, 3 x 7in, 3 x 4½, 2 x 4½in., mounted together on card, late 1920's. £528

An Amish pieced cotton quilted coverlet, Kalona, Iowa, 1921, worked in thirteen blocks of Star pattern with slate blue, maize and black fabrics and diamond and floral branch stitching, 74 x 80in. £2,784

A pieced silk quilted coverlet, probably Philadelphia, 1880-1900, centring a Rising Star in reds, green, white, purple and blue on a grey ground, 80 x 80in. £4,950

An unusual appliqued and embroidered cotton pictorial quilted coverlet, by Jennie C. Trein, Nazareth, Pennsylvania, 1932, centring a scene depicting a family Sunday picnic with gathering guests, a house in the background, boats in the water, and the family graveyard surrounded by an inner border with "Sunbonnet Sue" figures, 84 x 82in. £23,516

A pieced and embroidered silk and velvet coverlet, Lexington, Kentucky, 1880-1900, the contained Crazy Quilt pattern worked in various jewel-tone velvet fabrics and herringbone embroidery stitches with four centre blocks of eight-point stars enclosed by five concentric borders, 89 x 89in. £4,641

An Amish pieced cotton quilted coverlet, probably Indiana, circa 1930, the sixteen blocks each in the Broken Star pattern in blue, pink, purple and green on a black ground, 86 x 86in. £1,485

A fine pieced and appliqued cotton quilted coverlet, Palama Mission, Hawaii, 1899, centring a square reserve depicting the crest of the Hawaiian monarchy and inscribed "Ku'u Hae Aloha" surrounded by four Hawaiian flags and a yellow binding, 84 x 88in. £24,754

QUILTS

An Amish pieced cotton quilted coverlet, Midwestern, 1900-1925, worked in thirty blocks of Jacob's Ladder pattern with deep blue, purple, black, grey and brown fabrics, 76 x 89in. £1,175

A pieced wool quilted coverlet, Lancaster County, Pennsylvania, 1900-1910, worked in the Bars pattern in alternating light and dark brown surrounded by a red inner border with purple corners and grape and oak leaf stitching, 75 x 75in. £4,641

A Mennonite pieced wool quilted coverlet, Lancaster County, Pennsylvania, 1900-1925, worked in 100 blocks of Log Cabin pattern, each centring a green square surrounded by a quadruple border of alternating green and orange bands, 96 x 96in. £1,237

A pieced and embroidered wool coverlet, by Mary T. H. Willard, Evanston, Illinois, 1889, worked in a Crazy Quilt pattern in three vertical panels, each with polychrome fabrics embroidered with floral motifs and sentimental cross-stitch inscriptions of Biblical quotations, 67 x 85in. £6,807

An Amish pieced cotton quilted coverlet, Lancaster County, Pennsylvania, 1920-1940, worked in the Sunshine-and-Shadow pattern, with a spectrum of green, purple and pink blocks, surrounded by a wide slate blue border, 84 x 88in. £2,166

An Amish pieced wool quilted coverlet, Lancaster County, Pennsylvania, circa 1920, worked in the Diamond-in-the-Square pattern with mulberry and slate fabrics framed in deep pink and with a mulberry border and slate blue binding, 76 x 76in. £5,879

SHARE CERTIFICATES

Imperial Australian Corpn. Ltd., 1895, £1 shares, three vignettes. £184

Canada — The Province of Manitoba, 1885, £100 debenture with coupons, unsigned. £110

Folkestone Pier and Lift Co. 1888 £10 shares, vignette of Queen Victoria, Red seal. £32

Waveney Steam Drift Fishing Co. Ltd. 1909-18. Ord. £1 shares. £45

Pullman's Palace Car Company 1898, $100 shares. Vignette of St. Pancras Station and The Pullman Car Works, Detroit. £60

West Sunlight Reef Company, No Liability, Hillgrove, N.S.W. 1892, 10/- shares, Australian register. £50

BASKETS

An oval silver trompe-l'oeil basket, with twisted ropework handles, on four pierced feet, possibly by Piotr Loskutov, Moscow, 1882, 40cm. long, 723gr. £1,320

One of a set of seven Victorian two-handled baskets, by Carrington & Co., 1899 and 1900, one 17¾in. long, two 14in. long and two 12in. long, 212oz. £10,800

A shaped oval swing-handled cake basket with applied foliate border, Sheffield, 1914, 12in., 23oz. £264

A cake basket with pierced foliate handle, by Udall & Ballou, circa 1900-10, 11in. high overall, 14¾in. long, 49oz. £1,729

A Wiener Werkstatte electroplated basket, designed by Josef Hoffmann, 26cm. high. £990

An Unger Brothers basket, 24cm. across, stamped with monogram and Sterling 925 Fine, numbered 02616. £320

A massive Victorian oval basket, with cast scroll and acanthus handles, bearing plaques recording the 90th birthday of the Earl of Stradbroke, London 1878, 29in. long, 270oz. £34,000

A foliate pierced and fluted oval fruit basket, applied with rococo floral and foliate handles and with a scroll rim, London 1915, 8¾in., 22.50oz. £528

A late Victorian pierced moulded oval fruit basket chased with rococo floral and foliate swags, Charles Stuart Harris, London 1875, 13in., 31.75oz. £990

BOWLS

An Edwardian hammered
sugar bowl, in Art
Nouveau style, by A. E.
Jones, Birmingham, 1908,
4¼in. diam., 4.5oz. £100

A sterling silver bowl, by
Arthur Stone, 1910-37,
5.3/8in. diam., 7 troy oz.
£702

A punch bowl, the hemi-
spherical body divided into
arched panels, maker's mark
probably that of Chas. S.
Harris & Sons, 1929, 28.2cm.
diam., 37.5oz. £506

A heavy Celtic Revival bowl,
the almost hemispherical
body with a lightly hammered
finish, 1937 by the Gold-
smiths and Silversmiths Company Ltd., 17.5cm. across
handles, 13.3oz. £132

A good Japanese rose bowl,
of quatrefoil form, by Kunn
& Komor, circa 1900 (base
inscribed), 21.9cm. diam.
£1,250

A late Victorian punch bowl,
the lower part of the hemispherical body with swirl flutes,
1895, by Job Frank Hall of
Sibray, Hall and Co, 28.8cm.
diam., 31.5oz. £385

A Georg Jensen silver bowl,
supported on leaves and berried stems above a spreading
circular foot, 17.2cm. high.
£1,150

A 19th century Indian silver
deep bowl, 8½in. diam.,
33 troy oz. approx. £291

A Georg Jensen bowl and
cover, stamped with C. F.
Heise assay mark 100B and
with London import marks
for 1925, 11.9cm. high, 242gr.
£715

BOWLS

A Monteith bowl, by Samuel Kirk & Son, Baltimore, 1880-90, 5½in. high, 9½in. diam., 25oz. £864

A large two-handled circular bowl, by Elkington & Co., Birmingham, 1908, 13½in. diam., 100oz. £1,650

An Edwardian punch bowl, the hemispherical body with narrow vari-height flutes. Sheffield 1901 by Fenton Brothers Ltd. 27.5cm. diameter. 37.7oz. £935

A yachting trophy punch bowl, by Gorham Manuf. Co., 1884, the interior gilt, 9¼in. high, 18¼in. wide, 117oz. £25,272

A Hukin and Heath electroplated two handled bowl with hinged cover decorated with four engraved roundels of stylised floral motifs, designed by Dr C. Dresser and date code for 26th March 1879, 19.1cm. high. £9,900

Large plated punch bowl by Viners with embossed decoration. £45

A Georg Jensen footed bowl, stamped marks GJ 925.S 4, 7.6cm. high, 129.2gr. £374

A Georg Jensen footed bowl, hemispherical form with inverted rim, supported by eight foliate brackets on concave circular base, London import marks for 1930, 11.5cm. high, 505 grams. £638

A silver gilt bowl, by Gorham Manuf. Co., Providence, 1884, 3¾in. high, 6oz. £731

BOXES

A German decorative casket of rectangular bombe form, die stamped with masks within wreaths, import marks for 1897, psuedo 18th century Augsburg marks. £550

A silver gilt box, the lid inset with an enamel plaque, Birmingham hallmarks for 1922 and maker's monogram SB, 9cm. long, 2oz.17dwt. gross wt. £165

An A. E. Jones Arts and Crafts silver and copper jewellery casket, with a turquoise enamelled disc and pierced heart-shaped hinge, Birmingham hallmarks for 1929, 13.6cm. long. £660

A Victorian lozenge shaped plated biscuit box, with formal engraving and panel feet. £85

A rare stone set silver box with key by Tiffany & Company, New York, the hinged cover set with seven carved and polished amber stones, 3¼in. high, gross weight 22½oz. £4,548

A Liberty & Co. silver biscuit box with Birmingham hallmarks for 1902, 20oz.14dwt., 14cm. high. £432

An Arts & Crafts rectangular silver box, by W. Hutton & Sons Ltd., London hallmarks for 1901, 11.1cm. long, 11oz. 4dwt. gross weight. £242

A Danish white metal and ivory box and cover, stamped marks W/G and CF Heise assay mark, circa 1925, 13.5cm. high. £400

An unusual Sibyl Dunlop gemset rectangular silver box, embellished with scrollwork in relief, punctuated by square cabochons of rose quartz, 7.3cm. x 6.5cm., 1929. £650

BOXES

A Victorian casket of square bombe form, by S. S. Drew and E. Drew of J. Drew & Sons, 1890, 20.5cm. £550

A green stained box, by George Anton Scheidt, with pierced and chased white metal mount of scrolling tendrils, 6.3cm. long. £242

Early 20th century German silver singing bird box, 4in. long. £1,508

A shaped square silver casket, by Omar Ramsden, 1929, 4½in. high, 18oz.4dwt. £1,080

A Victorian Aesthetic Movement swing handled biscuit box, the curved body with twin fan shaped covers engraved with birds, circa 1880. £420

An unusual late 19th century German parcel gilt charity box, the hexagonal body modelled as a synagogue, circa 1880, 10cm. high, 2ozs. £450

A sterling silver box with pierced enamel hinged cover, Worcester, Mass., 1925, 3¾in. wide. £256

An Arts & Crafts hammered silver box, by Chas. Horner, Birmingham hallmarks for 1902, 15.3cm. long, 5oz. 12dwt. £440

An attractive late 19th century French enamel and silver gilt box depicting courting couples in 18th century costume, circa 1890, 5.2cm. long. £320

CANDELABRA

One of a pair of five-light candelabra, by Tiffany & Co., New York, 1885-91, 18¾in. high, 133oz.10dwt. £11,306

One of a pair of Georg Jensen candelabra with five cup-shaped candle nozzles and circular drip pans supported on U-shaped branches, 27cm. high. £21,600

One of a pair of late 19th century German cast rococo style seven-light candelabra, by J. D. Schleissner & Sons, Hanau, 54cm. high, 234.5oz. £3,500

A pair of George I style three light candelabra, each on hexagonal base with scroll branches, by Richard Comyns, 1964, 71ozs, 11¼in. high. £1,540

One of a pair of Georg Jensen five-branch candelabra, designed by Harald Nielsen, 40cm. high. £15,400

A pair of Art Nouveau plated metal figural candlesticks, designed by C. Bonnefond, each modelled as a girl with long hair, 36.5cm. high. £1,300

A Hagenauer chromium plated four branch candelabra, the forked tubular branches on knopped stem, 50.7cm. high. £2,420

A pair of late Victorian silver three light candelabra, London 1896, maker's mark Thomas Bradbury of Sheffield, 46cm. high, weight of branches 64¾oz. £1,450

A two-branch candelabrum, designed by Soren Georg Jensen, 17.7cm. high, 26oz.10dwt. £1,430

CANDLESTICKS

One of a pair of Georg Jensen candlesticks, designed by S. Bernadotte, 6cm. high, 8oz.16dwt. **£605**

A pair of silver candlesticks with rococo and floral embossing, Edinburgh, 1893, 4½in. high. **£240**

One of a pair of Liberty & Co. three-branch silver wall sconces, with Birmingham hallmarks for 1901, 29oz., 20cm. high. **£1,188**

Pair of late Victorian candlesticks, formed as Corinthian columns, by Charles Stuart Harris, London, 1898, 29cm. high, weighted. **£800**

A pair of Victorian novelty bedroom candlesticks, each modelled as three grotesque faces; one sleeping, one yawning and one smiling; 21cm. high, by Henry William Dee, 1878, 19½ozs. **£4,400**

A pair of James Dixon & Sons silver candlesticks, Sheffield hallmarks for 1904, 22cm. high. **£825**

A pair of late Victorian candlesticks, each on shaped square base, by William Hutton and Son Ltd., 1900, 11½in. high. **£715**

Two of four silver candlesticks, by Omar Ramsden, two 1919, two 1922, loaded, 22.5cm. high. **£3,000**

Pair of silver candlesticks, decorated in the Adam style, by John Round & Sons Ltd., Sheffield, 1902, 6½in. tall. **£410**

211

CASTERS

An early 18th century style
lighthouse sugar caster on
a skirted foot, London, 1932,
7in. high, 9oz.   £132

A Continental caster modelled
as a kingfisher, import hallmarks for Glasgow, 1908,
16cm. from beak to tail. £175

An Edwardian plain baluster
sugar caster, by Elkington &
Co., Birmingham, 1909, 8in.
high, 12oz.   £154

An Edwardian hammered
baluster sugar caster by
Ramsden & Carr with bun-
top, 1907, 17.5cm. high,
8ozs.   £575

A sugar caster designed by
Harald Nielsen, stamped
Dessin H.N. 925S Georg
Jensen S Wendel A/S 645,
circa 1949, 11.4cm. high,
7oz.14dwt.   £432

A plain cylindrical sugar
caster with domed cover,
by Goldsmiths & Silversmiths
Co., London, 1911, 7¼in.
high, 11.50oz.   £150

An Omar Ramsden hammered
silver sugar caster, the elabora-
tely pierced cover with beaded
rim and Galleon plaque, London
hallmarks for 1936, 15.3cm. high,
250 grams.   £1,430

An amber, coral and mala-
chite sugar caster, designed
by Anton Rosen, stamped
marks GJ 826 GJ, 19.9cm.
high.   £2,200

A large inverted pear shaped
sugar caster, the body
decorated with two friezes of
flowers and foliage, Arthur
and Frank Parsons, London
1927, 9½in., 14.75oz. £385

CENTREPIECES

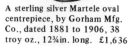

A WMF electroplated centrepiece with cut glass liner of
oval section modelled in full
relief with young lovers,
21in. across. £638

A sterling silver Martele oval
centrepiece, by Gorham Mfg.
Co., dated 1881 to 1906, 38
troy oz., 12¾in. long. £1,636

A WMF plated centrepiece of
twin-handled boat-shape with
clear glass liner, 46cm. long.
£420

An Austro-Hungarian brightly
coloured silver gilt centrepiece
finely modelled as a crowned
ostrich, by Hermann Bohm,
Vienna, circa 1880, 15in. high.
£19,800

A Victorian plated centrepiece base, the
simulated coral mount supported by
three dolphins, 11in. high, together
with a matching pair of single dolphin
centrepiece bases, 8in. high. £330

A Victorian parcel gilt centrepiece and mirror plateau, by
F. Elkington, Birmingham,
1893, 27in. high, 207oz.
£4,860

An unusual Victorian oval
centrepiece with cut glass bowl
with shaped rim, with several
diamond registration marks
for the 29th March 1876,
overall height 9½in. £770

A baroque style centrepiece,
Sheffield, 1903, approx.
20in. high, approx. 158oz.
£2,900

Early 20th century French
silver gilt centrepiece, Paris,
maker's mark AD, bird
between, 10¾in. high, 134oz.
£4,649

CHAMBERSTICKS

SILVER

An Art Nouveau oil chamberstick with leaf-capped loop handle, 14.25cm. diam.   £300

A Tiffany & Co unusual late 19th century American Aesthetic Movement parcel gilt chamberstick, with incurved sides, circa 1880, 11ozs.   £6,000

One of a set of four Victorian plain circular chamber candlesticks, by Robt. Garrard, 1878, 7in. diam., 63oz.   £3,850

CHOCOLATE POTS

A sterling silver Martele chocolate pot, by Gorham Mfg. Co., circa 1900, 11½in. high, 23 troy oz.   £2,083

A cylindrical chocolate pot, by S. C. S. Groth, Copenhagen, 1884, 17.5cm. high, 17oz. £285

A silver chocolate pot by Tiffany & Company, New York, tapering cylindrical and partly reeded, on a moulded circular foot, marked, 9¼in. high, gross weight 31oz.   £1,949

CIGARETTE BOXES

An Alfred Dunhill silver gilt and enamel cigarette box and lighter, London hallmarks for 1929.   £756

Silver cigarette box and cover, in the Art Nouveau style, by Ramsden & Carr, circa 1903, 7½in. wide.   £750

A cigarette box, by Ramsden and Carr, the bowed handhammered sides with applied entrelac band, London, 1908, 3¾ x 3¼in.   £650

CIGARETTE CASES

A white metal and enamel
cigarette case, the enamel
by F. Zwichl, circa 1920.
£1,944

A Russian cigarette case with
separate hinged vesta com-
partment, probably by Dmitri
Nikolaiev, Moscow, circa 1890.
£230

A late Victorian cigarette case
enamelled on cover with a
coaching scene, by J. Wilmot,
Birmingham, 1896.   £280

A cigarette case, the cover cast
with Napoleon mounted on a
rearing horse, white metal, by
Konstantin Skvortsov, Moscow,
1908-1917, 4½in. long, 204.6gr.
£440

Late 19th century Austrian
enamel cigarette case, the
cover enamelled with an
Ancient Egyptian scene,
circa 1895.   £600

A Samorodok cigarette case,
with cabochon sapphire gold
mounted thumbpiece, white
metal, by Ivan Arkharov, St.
Petersburg, 1898-1903, 9.5cm.
172.8gr. gross.   £286

A German cigarette case
enamelled on cover with a
spaniel carrying a dead duck
in its mouth, circa 1900.
£250

A French Art Deco lacquered
and eggshell cigarette case, with
broad band of crushed eggshell
reserved against a black background, 10.3cm.   £200

A late Victorian gilt lined
cigarette case, enamelled with
a scene from R. Kipling's poem
'Absent minded beggar', C.S. &
F.S., Birmingham, 1899. £250

CIGARETTE CASES

An Austrian cigarette case applied with two-colour gold and gem set monograms and facsimile signatures, circa 1895. £520

A good 19th century Russian niello cigarette case, cover depicting a despatch carrier being driven by a peasant in a horse-drawn carriage, Gustav Klingert, Moscow, 1888, 8.5cm. long. £340

A Victorian cigarette case, the cover enamelled with a nude girl lying beside a stream, Birmingham, 1887. £400

An Art Nouveau hammered silver cigarette box, decorated in relief with an Art Nouveau maiden within a keyhole reserve, with Chester hallmarks for 1902, 12.5cm. long. £286

A Portuguese enamel cigarette case, the cover depicting a bare-breasted Classical girl, circa 1900. £380

A Soviet propaganda cigarette case, the foreground with crossed banners and Red Star, white metal, Moscow, 1927, 4½in. long, 162.8gr. gross. £825

A Continental plated cigarette case enamelled with a collie dog on a sky background, circa 1910. £150

A stylish Art Deco cigarette case, formed by geometric segments of black, brown, brick-red and silver coloured metal, 10.7cm. £150

An Edwardian gilt lined cigarette case, polychrome-enamelled with a picture of a lady, R.C., Birmingham, 1905. £200

CLARET JUGS

A mounted cut glass claret jug, engraved with the initial Z, white metal, marked Faberge, with Imperial warrant, Moscow, 1899-1908, 9in. high. £935

A Victorian novelty clear glass claret jug, formed as a seal, the hinged silver head and neck realistically chased with fur and inset with glass eyes, by William Leuchars, 1881, 12½in. long. £2,420

An Elkington & Co. plated claret jug, designed by Christopher Dresser, date letter for 1885, 24.4cm. high. £25,000

A Victorian silver and etched glass claret jug, by George Fox, London, 1895, with repousse and chased silver spout, 12½in. high. £355

A Hukin and Heath silver and glass claret jug, designed by Christopher Dresser, marked JWH/JTH for London 1879, 22.2cm. high. £1,100

A Victorian pear-shaped claret jug, on domed foot, by Richard Martin and Ebenezer Hall, 1877, 14in. high. (gross 44ozs.) £1,430

A late Victorian claret jug, the oval diamond cut glass body etched with a golfer in full swing, circa 1880, 25.5cm. high. £880

A mounted cut-glass claret jug, the tapering cylindrical glass body with stellar motif, white metal, marked Khlebnikov, with Imperial warrant, St. Petersburg, 1908-1917, 11¾in. high, 1263.8gr. gross. £1,540

A rare, mounted glass, ovoid shaped claret jug on circular foot with coronet pierced gallery collar, 34.5cm. high, 1922. £6,000

COFFEE POTS

A Georgian style coffee pot, the domed hinged cover with ivory oval mushroom knop, Sheffield, 1891, 24½oz. £380

A silver Martele coffee pot by Gorham Manufacturing Company, Providence, 1899, of baluster form, 10¼in. high, 32oz. £2,274

Early 20th century repousse decorated sterling silver coffee pot, Gorham Mfg. Co., 12.7/8in. high, approx. 26 troy oz. £718

CREAM JUGS

A silver oval covered cream jug, by Omar Ramsden, 1925, 11cm. high, 8.5oz. £800

A Victorian novelty cream jug, modelled as a Chinaman, the handle his plaited hair, maker Thomas Smiley, London 1882, 2.5oz. £440

A Georg Jensen silver cream jug, supported on three foliate feet and having a leaf and magnolia bloom handle, 7.5cm. high. £220

CRUETS

An Elkington three piece cruet and holder, the design attributed to Dr Christopher Dresser, with slender column and T-shaped handle, 12.7cm. high. £198

A fine electroplated trefoil decanter stand, the three cylindrical bottle holders pierced with scroll foliage below shaped moulded rims, by Elkington and Co., with date letter for 1911, 34.8cm. £715

A Hukin & Heath silver condiment set designed by Dr. C. Dresser, London hallmarks for 1881, 14.2cm. high. £1,045

CUPS

A Georg Jensen hammered silver and amethyst cup and cover, Copenhagen mark and London import marks for 1926, 19.9cm. high. £4,400

A late Victorian stirrup cup modelled as a fox's head, with circular cartouche, by Elkington & Co., Birmingham, 1897, 7.25oz. £978

A late Victorian neo-classical style two-handled trophy cup, by Charles S. Harris, London, 1899, 15in. high, 81oz. £530

A silver gilt replica of the Norton Cup In The Fishmonger's Company, dated 1925, by Gerrard and Co Ltd., 1918, 14in. high, 49ozs. £880

A German white metal large three-handled cup and cover, by J. H. Werner, circa 1905, 26½in. high, 10kg. £4,950

A cup and cover in the early 17th century style, the gold plaque engraved 'The Manchester Cup 1924', 1923, 15ct., in fitted case, 17¼in. high, 54oz. £19,800

A Victorian silver gilt cup, by Alfred Clark, in the manner of J. H. Hunt, 19in. high, London, 1879. £950

A two handled cup applied with Celtic style frieze and boss decoration incorporating various gem stones, height without plinth, 7in., 40.25oz. £880

A presentation loving cup, by Dominick & Haff, Newark, for J. E. Caldwell & Co., 1895, in original mahogany box, 11½in. high, 82oz. £5,985

DISHES

A Joel F. Hewes sterling silver hand-raised, footed candy dish, circa 1908, 6in. diam., approx. 10 troy oz. **£238**

An Omar Ramsden hammered silver tazza, the shallow circular bowl with inverted rim and scalloped sides, with maker's marks and London hallmarks for 1925, 22.3cm. diam. 927 grams. **£1,650**

An enamelled sterling silver and glass jam dish and spoon, by Mary P. Winlock, 4.5/8in. diam., approx. 5 troy oz. **£297**

A pair of entree dishes and covers, rounded rectangular with gadrooned borders and domed pull-off covers, 11in. wide, London, 1938, 97oz. **£1,200**

A Hukin and Heath silver sugar basin designed by Dr Christopher Dresser, with hinged loop handle, the hemispherical bowl with raised double-rib decoration, with stamped maker's marks and London hallmarks for 1879, 12.5cm. diam. 182 grams. **£3,960**

A pair of Edwardian bon-bon dishes, Chester, 1901, 172gr. total. **£140**

A late Victorian dish, by Walker & Hall, Sheffield, 1898, 24cm. diam., 330gr. **£170**

A shell-shaped bonbonniere on triple ball feet, Sheffield, 1910, 6½in. long, 6oz. **£150**

One of a set of twelve plates, by Redlich & Co., New York, circa 1900, 9¾in. diam., 160oz. **£3,192**

FLATWARE

Part of a 140-piece mixed metal flatware service, by Tiffany & Co., 1880-85, dinner fork, 8.1/8in. long, ladel 13in. long, 201oz. 10dwt. excluding knives. £59,855

Part of a 24-piece set of parcel gilt dessert knives and forks, by Tiffany & Co., circa 1880-85, knives 8¼in. long, 48oz.10dwt. £2,992

Three of seven parcel gilt condiment servers, by Tiffany & Co., circa 1880-85, serving spoon 9½in. long, sauce ladles each approx. 7in. long, 13oz. £3,657

Part of an International Co. partial sterling silver flatware service, Meriden, Conn., circa 1934, consisting of 53 pieces, weight approx. 110 troy oz. £648

Part of a Georg Jensen 36-piece 'Acorn' pattern table service, designed by Johan Rohde. £1,870

A set of four parcel gilt serving pieces, by Tiffany & Co., circa 1880-85, ladle 13½in. long, 18oz.10dwt. £5,653

FRAMES

An Art Nouveau silver picture frame, 35cm. high, marked WN and for Chester 1903. £360

A Wm. Hutton & Sons Arts & Crafts silver picture frame, London hallmarks for 1903, 20cm. high. £1,485

A Wm. Hutton & Sons Arts & Crafts silver picture frame, London hallmarks for 1903, 20cm. high. £1,430

An Edwardian Art Nouveau silver and enamel photograph frame, Wm. Hutton & Sons Ltd., London, 1904, 10.25in. high, also an Elkington & Co. vase, Birmingham, 1906. £750

A Liberty & Co. silver and enamelled picture frame, 19 x 14.50cm., with Art Nouveau hinged support, hallmarked L. & Co., Birmingham, 1899. £1,850

A William Hutton & Sons silver and enamel picture frame, with repousse decoration and entre-lac motif, London hallmarks for 1903, 20.4cm. high. £990

A Ramsden & Carr silver picture frame, with London hallmarks for 1900, 15.5cm. high. £950

A William Hutton & Sons silver and enamelled picture frame, embellished with tendrils and blue and green enamelling, 9cm. high, London 1904. £320

An embossed and pierced shaped silver photograph frame, London, 1900, 8in. high. £180

SILVER

GOBLETS

A China Trades gilt lined goblet chased with flowering prunus on a crackled ground, Wang Hing, 6in. high. £220

A large goblet designed by H. Nielsen, stamped Dessin H.N. G.J. 535, circa 1928, 19.9cm. high, 25oz.15dwt. £1,725

A 20th century enamelled and jewelled sterling silver chalice, approx. 4 troy oz. £376

A plated trophy goblet by Pairpoint, New Bedford, last quarter 19th century, the interior gilt, marked, 12in. high. £623

Two late 19th century Chinese Colonial silver wine goblets, struck with maker's mark WF and an ideogram, 7½in. and 7.5/8in. high, 20oz.10dwt. £548

One of two Edwardian silver gilt goblets, by Edward Barnard & Sons Ltd., 1902 and 1903, 10¼in. high, 46oz. £990

An Arts & Crafts Movement chalice in medieval style, by Omar Ramsden & Alwin Carr, London, 1912, 5.2in. high, 10oz. all in. £760

An Arts and Crafts silver two handled goblet by Skinner & Co., the flared bowl with knopped base, with London hallmarks for 1907, 14.5cm. high, 309 grams. £242

An Omar Ramsden beaten silver goblet, the foot with inscription MCMXXI, 5in. high, London hallmarks for 1920. £180

223

INKSTANDS

A shaped rectangular inkstand, the cut glass bottles with shaped circular silver caps, Sheffield, 1905, maker's mark WM&S, 27.6cm. long, 20.8oz. £484

An attractive silver and tortoise-shell inkstand, inlaid with rosettes and floral swags, London 1910, by William Comyns. £740

An 18th century Victorian gadrooned rounded oblong inkstand, on curved legs, Goldsmiths & Silversmiths Co. Ltd., London 1899, 8¾in., 22oz. free. £528

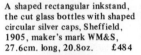

A Victorian Scottish inkwell, by Aitchison of Edinburgh, 1885, inkwell 15cm. high. £900

A silver oblong inkstand with flat hinged lid, the interior with two glass inkwells and silver dip pen, 9in. wide, Birmingham 1918, 32oz. £275

A Guild of Handicraft white metal and enamel inkwell, attributed to C. R. Ashbee, seven sided on ball feet, 10.5cm. high. £1,728

A late Victorian shaped oblong inkstand on hoof feet, fitted with two silver topped cut-glass square inkwells, W. G. & J. L., London 1898, 10¾in. wide., 33oz. £1,045

A late Victorian rectangular inkstand, the three quarter gallery pierced with scroll foliage, 1895 by William Hutton and Sons Ltd., 29.7cm. across, 26oz. weighable silver. £935

An oblong inkstand with pierced gallery and gadroon borders, London 1902, weighable silver 30oz., 12in. long. £1,150

JUGS

Early 20th century Arthur Stone sterling silver water pitcher, Gardner, Mass., 9in. high, 31 troy oz. £1,081

A plain oval silver milk jug, marked Faberge, with Imperial warrant, St. Petersburg, circa 1880, 2¾in. high, 168.9gr. £418

A Christofle electroplated jug, mounted with an unpierced wooden handle, the base stamped with marks and Gallia, prod. Christofle, Italy, 22.5cm. high. £242

A silver water jug, the bulbous form decorated with a frieze of repousse laurel leaves, the handle in the shape of a rampant leopard, with London import marks for 1973, 23cm. high, 2,090 grams. £660

A large pear shaped silver water jug, the body repousse and chased with rococo cartouche enriched with flowering blossoms, marked Faberge, with Imperial warrant, Moscow, 1891, 11in. high, 2208.4gr. £3,850

A silver water pitcher, attributed to Dominick & Haff, New York, circa 1880, with an everted brim and a scroll handle, marked Sterling on base, 6¾in. high. £974

A jug with ebony handle, stamped Georg Jensen 407A, 23.2cm. high, 35oz. 5dwt. gross weight. £1,836

A pitcher of baluster form with an open handle, by Gorham Manuf. Co., 1897, 8¾in. high, gross weight 31oz. £1,306

An Elkington & Co. electroplated jug designed by Dr. C. Dresser, 19.3cm. high. £1,296

MISCELLANEOUS

A napkin ring, repousse and chased with two bogatyrs, dated 1911, white metal, by Mikhail Tarasov, Moscow, 1908-1917, 38.3gr. £220

A Hukin & Heath electroplated letter rack designed by Dr. C. Dresser, stamped H & H 2555 and registration lozenge for May 1881, 12.3cm. high. £280

A Liberty & Co. 'Cymric' silver belt buckle, set with an oval cabochon lapis lazuli, stamped 'Cymric', L & Co and Birmingham hallmarks for 1900, 11cm. long. £330

A silver, onyx and coral paper knife and book mark, signed Cartier, London, 1934, 14cm. £198

A pair of plique-a-jour enamelled and gilt beakers, by P. Ovchinnikov with the Imperial warrant, Moscow, 1899-1908, 3¾in. high. £4,950

A silver flask by Whiting Manufacturing Company, circa 1885, the front repousse and chased with a seahorse, 6in. long, 7½oz. £1,689

A Victorian shaped dressing table mirror with easel support, by William Comyns, London, 1893, 10¾in. high. £385

Three pieces from a dressing table set, die stamped with foliage in the Art Nouveau style, Chester 1903/04/05, by W. Neale. £77

A late 19th century English electrotype shield with scenes from John Bunyan's 'Pilgrim's Progress', electroformed from the original by L. Morel-Ladeuil by Elkington & Co. £1,430

MISCELLANEOUS

An American silver bottle cradle by the Gorham Co., 1890, oval with gadrooned borders, 13½in. long. £1,031

A parcel gilt punch service, with repousse and chased view of the Kremlin, by Antip Kuzmichev, Moscow, 1882, the tray 12½in. wide, 3486.4gr. £3,850

Edwardian novelty desk clip and pen brush in the form of a muzzled bear, Birmingham, 1908. £280

Late 19th century Victorian silver plated three-bottle decanter stand, by Martin Hall & Co., 13½in. high. £290

A Russian table lighter of urn or tureen shape by Karl Faberge, decorated with swags and bead borders, circa 1910, 9.8cm. high. £700

A silver mounted walking stick watch, the movement with cylinder escapement, signed Ludvig Holuska, the white enamel dial with Roman numerals, 1899, 35½in. £902

A George V two handled bottle holder of cylindrical form pierced and cast with stylised flower heads, London 1910, 535 grammes, 16.5cm. high. £340

A Tiffany sterling silver sealing wax set, N.Y., circa 1891-1902, 8½in. sq., wt. approx. 20 troy oz. £432

A good Continental silver-gilt and enamel aide-de-memoire, enamelled with a rower in student's cap, probably German, circa 1895. £580

227

MISCELLANEOUS

A Liberty hammered silver and enamelled belt buckle, the pierced floral decoration enamelled in blue and green, Birmingham hall marks for 1910. 7.5cm. long. **£550**

A Victorian Scottish silver mounted ram's head snuff mull, on three castors, with various attachments, Edinburgh, 1881, height overall 12in. **£1,760**

An Edwardian crouching rabbit pin cushion, by Adie & Lovekin Ltd., Birmingham, 1907. **£140**

A Georg Jensen tazza, stamped marks 264B GJ 925 S and London import marks for 1928, 30.5cm. high, 1.701kg. **£3,520**

A silver tea glass holder, with applied troika horse heads, by V. Akimov, Moscow, circa 1900, overall 4¾in. high, with glass liner, 206.9gr. **£495**

A large easel mirror with bevelled rectangular plate in ornamental trellis and scroll, Chester, 1898, makers J.D. and W.D., 19 x 12½in. **£400**

A French silver gilt mounted spirit flask, the glass body etched with scroll foliage, late 19th/early 20th century, 13.6cm. **£154**

An unusual German silver casket, the front with two doors pierced with figures, import marks for 1892, sponsor's mark of Joseph Morpurgo, 14.7cm. high. **£418**

A covered tazza designed by J. Rohde, stamped Dessin J.R. Georg Jensen 43, circa 1920, 15.5cm. high, 14oz. 9dwt. **£1,080**

MODELS

A German decorative silver carriage, import marks for 1901, sponsor's mark of John George Piddington, 12.7cm.
£286

A late Victorian novelty port bottle carrier in the form of a donkey and cart, 13in. long, by H. T., London, 1890.
£940

A silver cast model of a Clydesdale horse, the sculptor G. Halliday, made by Elkington & Co., Birmingham, 1911, 21in. high, 309oz.
£9,720

'Vestal' a silvered bronze figure by Le Faguays, on stepped square shaped marble base, 14½in. high.
£1,100

A Continental silver metal figure of a curly haired youth, on black marble plinth, 29.5cm. high, and another group of a younger child, 30cm. high.
£850

'Nude Girl with Shawl', a silvered bronze figure cast from a model by Lorenzl, decorated by Crejo, 37.5cm. high.
£1,296

A late 19th century English silvered bronze group of a jockey on horseback, signed and dated J. Willis Good, 1875, 27cm. high.
£2,500

A Continental silver model of a grouse, by B. Muller, import marks for 1902, 10½in. high, 26oz.
£1,134

A late 19th century English silvered bronze group of a jockey on horseback, signed and dated J. Willis Good, 1875, 32.5cm. high.
£2,000

MUGS

A Victorian christening mug with loop handle, W. E., London, 1878, 4½in. high. £160

A Victorian gilt-lined baluster christening mug on spreading circular foot, engraved with a monogram and date, circa 1891, 4in. high. £220

A silver applied enamelled copper mug, by Gorham Manuf. Co., Providence, 1881, 6½in. high. £1,154

MUSTARDS

A mixed metal mustard pot by Dominick & Haff, New York, 1880, the surface engraved in an all over blossom pattern, 6.04cm. high, gross weight 3oz. £584

A C. R. Ashbee silver mustard pot, set with six turquoise cabochons, London hallmarks for 1900, 8cm. high. £864

A Guild of Handicrafts silver mustard pot, designed by C. R. Ashbee, with London hallmarks for 1902, 8.5cm. high, 4oz.11dwt. gross weight. £918

SALTS

Two of a set of four Hukin & Heath silver salts with salt spoons, Birmingham hallmarks for 1879, 6oz. 4dwt. each 3.4cm. high. £864

A pair of knife rests and open salts, by Tiffany & Co., 1878-91, also a set of four butter plates, each approx. 3in. wide, 13oz. £1,862

Pair of late Victorian salt cellars by Hunt & Roskell Ltd., 1901, 6½in. high, 34oz. £5,280

SAUCEBOATS

 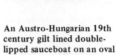 

A good quality silver sauce-boat, with leaf capped double scroll handle, London 1901, by the Barnards, 8½in. long, 15oz. £240

An Austro-Hungarian 19th century gilt lined double-lipped sauceboat on an oval stand, 9¾in. wide, 23.25oz. £242

One of a pair of late Victorian cast shell-shape sauceboats, by Charles S. Harris, London, 1897. £460

TANKARDS

  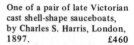

A German large tapering flagon, by Korner & Proll, Berlin, late 19th century, 15¼in. high, 3330gr. £2,750

A silver mounted leather 'blackjack', by Gorham Manuf. Co., Providence, circa 1905, 7½in. high. £199

A repousse tankard, by Tiffany & Co., N.Y. finished March 10, 1893, for the World's Columbian Exposition, Chicago, 1893, 10in. high, 52oz. 10dwt. £17,291

TEA CADDIES

A Ramsden & Carr silver tea-caddy and spoon, London hallmarks for 1931, 10.9cm. high, 13oz.7dwt. gross wt. £1,650

A Continental late 19th century oblong tea caddy in the George II taste, chased with a vignette of a woman picking tea leaves, import marks for Sheffield 1896, 5¾in., 12oz. £495

A Victorian tea caddy, maker George Fox, London, 1874, 5in. high. £560

231

TEA & COFFEE SETS

A stylish Mexican Art Deco five piece tea set designed in the manner of Jean Puiforcat, each vessel of broad cylindrical shape. £2,800

A late Victorian five piece engraved tea and coffee service of panelled design with pleated bodies and ivory handles and finials, by Harison Bros. & Howson of Sheffield, 1885/6, 82oz. £2,200

A Victorian tea and coffee service, comprising pear-shaped teapot, coffee pot, hot water jug, sugar basin and cream jug, on a two-handled shaped oval tray, by Elkington & Co., Birmingham 1897 and 1898, the tray 24¾in. long, gross 234oz. £6,600

Victorian silver three-piece tea service having engraved and repousse decoration, maker JA, 46 troy oz., London 1875/77. £500

A five-piece tea service and tray, by Tiffany & Co., New York, circa 1881, comprising a coffee pot, a covered sugar bowl, a cream pitcher, a waste bowl and a large two-handled tray, coffee pot 8½in. high, tray 27¼in. long, gross weight 306oz. £24,272

A six-piece tea and coffee service, by Bigelow, Kennard & Co., Boston, circa 1901, kettle 12in. high, gross weight 168oz. £2,757

TEA KETTLES

A Victorian style part-fluted compressed tea kettle with a burner, probably George Fox, London 1912, 11½in., 45oz.
£550

A Victorian swing-handle compressed tea kettle engraved with scrolling foliage, with a burner, 13¾in. high.
£352

A Victorian inverted pear-shaped tea kettle, stand and lamp, by Harris Bros., 1896, gross 63oz.
£880

A late Victorian part fluted and gadrooned moulded oblong tea kettle with rising curved spout, W.S. & C.S., Sheffield 1900, 14¾in. overall, 54oz. gross.
£660

An F. Minsfiberg kettle-on-stand with ivory handle and ivory finial, 29.2cm. high.
£1,650

A moulded shaped oblong tea kettle with panelled rising curved spout and ebonised wood handle, by Charles Stuart Harris & Son, London 1911, 13in., 42.25oz. gross.
£495

A Victorian circular kettle on stand, the underframe with a spirit heater, maker's mark two bells, 16.5in. high. £420

A Continental fluted pear shaped swing handled tea kettle chased with flowers and foliage, 8¾in. overall.
£187

A Victorian silver tea kettle, stand and burner, the kettle of oval lobed form with part fluting, Sheffield 1895, makers Mappin Brothers, 38½oz. £560

SILVER

TEAPOTS

A silver pear shaped teapot, fluted, on four foliate capped scroll feet, by Sazikov, Moscow, circa 1890, 4¼in., 280.5gr. £638

An unusual part fluted tapering teapot with rising curved spout, the base engraved: "Patent Trade S.Y.P. Mark Teapot", James Dixon & Son, Sheffield 1912, 9¼in., 42oz. gross. £528

A reeded fluted oval teapot in the George III taste, with a fluted rising curved spout, Elkington and Co., Birmingham 1916, 5¾in., 16oz. gross. £275

TOAST RACKS

A Hukin & Heath electro-plated toast rack, designed by C. Dresser, 5¼in. high. £1,430

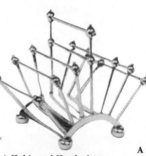

A Hukin and Heath electro-plated letter stand designed by Dr Christopher Dresser, the convex base on four bun feet, the middle support raised to a handle, registration mark for 9 May 1881, 12.5cm. high.
£418

A rare James Dixon & Sons electroplated toastrack designed by Dr Christopher Dresser, the rectangular frame with seven triangular supports, each with angular wire decoration, 16.4cm. high. £14,300

A Hukin & Heath plated toastrack, attributed to Christopher Dresser with open rectangular base supported on block feet, 11.5cm. high. £560

A Hukin & Heath plated toastrack designed by Christopher Dresser with rectangular base, having seven sets of rod divisions, 13.7cm. high. £3,200

A Charles Boynton silver toast-rack of oval, almost boat shape, 9.5cm. high, 5.5oz., marked CB for London 1936. £350

TRAYS & SALVERS

A sterling silver strapwork tray, signed Shreve & Co. San Francisco Sterling, circa 1918, 12½in. diam., 26 troy oz. £378

A Japanese Export silver tray, 19th century, with cut corners, the convex rim applied with dragons in high relief, 26in. long, approximate weight 114 troy oz. £2,366

A silver footed salver having fancy border, Sheffield, 1934, 12in. diam., 27 troy oz. £300

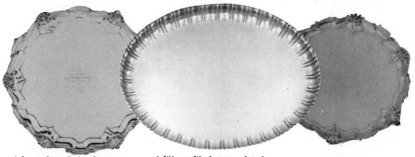

A large shaped circular presentation salver, the raised moulded rim with scroll leafage, 1912 by Edward Barnard and Sons, 51cm. diam. £748

A Wiener Werkstatte plated oval tray, designed by Josef Hoffmann, embellished with vertical lobes and fluting, 34cm. wide. £800

A silver footed salver having fancy border, London, 1912, 15in. diam., 46 troy oz. £525

Late 19th century silver mounted shibayama inlaid lacquer tray, signed Yasuaki, 24cm. diam. £1,650

A silver footed two-handled tray with rope edge, Birmingham, 1930, 21 x 13in., 56 troy oz. £460

An inlaid waiter with an everted brim, on four cast feet, by Tiffany & Co., 1878-91, 9½in. diam., gross weight 10oz. £11,971

TUREENS

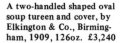

A tureen and cover designed by Georg Jensen, stamped Georg Jensen 337B, 132.5cm. wide, 63oz.16dwt.   £18,360

A two-handled shaped oval soup tureen and cover, by Elkington & Co., Birmingham, 1909, 126oz.   £3,240

A Hukin & Heath electro-plated soup tureen and cover, designed by Dr. C. Dresser, 31cm. diam.   £2,808

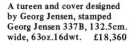

A tureen with domed cover, by Black, Starr & Frost, New York, circa 1900, 9½in. high, 14in. wide overall, 73oz.10dwt.   £2,128

A Victorian soup tureen and cover, by T. W. H. & H. Dobson, 1880, 30cm. across handles, 46.5oz.   £1,045

A plated soup tureen by Meriden Britannia Company, Meriden, 1875-1885, in the Japanese taste, with a flaring brim, together with a plated ladle by Rogers Brothers, tureen 17in. wide.   £519

URNS

A 19th century plated samovar of globular form with lion ring handles, on four ball feet, 14in. high.   £75

A French two handled fluted pear shaped coffee urn and stand, the tap formed as the mask of Bacchus with shell terminal, circa 1880, maker's mark G.F., 18½in.high. 2.13gr. gross.   £1,375

An Art Deco chromium plated tea urn of tapering form, 42cm. high, stamped 'REG 849217'.   £520

VASES

An Art Nouveau baluster vase chased with lilies of the valley, the base impressed with a date 1896, 7¼in., 14.75oz. £275

Hallmarked silver posy holder, with blue glass liner, Sheffield, 1904. £80

A silver twin-handled vase, 16.6cm. high, 12.5oz., stamped E.J.B. maker's marks, Birmingham, 1909. £280

A silver double vase on stand, by The Sweetser Co., New York, circa 1900-15, the stand of copper, 11½in. high, gross wt. of vase 20oz.10dwt. £1,084

A pair of Continental vases, modelled as double-ended cornucopiae, the rims pierced with rococo scrolls, 1897, 28cm. long, 20cm. high, 41.5ozs. £1,650

A Liberty silver vase, the design attributed to A. Knox, stamped Cymric. L & Co within three lozenges and with Birmingham hallmarks for 1907, 17cm. high. £270

An ovoid vase, by Tiffany & Co., N.Y., 1878-90, 6.5/8in. high, 14oz. £4,322

A pair of crocus-shaped embossed silver vases with leaf decoration, 6¼in. high. £100

Late 19th century shaped octagonal silver vase and cover with eight oval lacquer panels, signed Haruaki, 46cm. high. £12,100

238

SILVER

A 19th century Turkish parcel-gilt vase of fluted, campana shape with applied surround of birds, flowers and leaves, 13.5cm high, 12oz.   £400

Goldsmiths and Silversmiths Company: Replica of the Warwick Vase, 8in. high, on square base, London, 1912, 65oz.   £1,800

A large Eastern vase on a lobed hexafoil base with applied floral and shell feet, 20½in. high.   £462

A tapering cylindrical vase, with a roundel enclosing a collie's head in relief, by I. Marshak, St Petersburg, 1908-1917, 7½in. high, 424.1gr.   £1,045

A Continental suite of three gadrooned tapering vases pierced and chased with rococo flowers and scrolling foliage, 10¾in. and 6½in.   £1,100

A Liberty & Co. 'Cymric' silver and enamel vase, the body decorated with a band of blue and orange enamelled stylised fruit branches, Birmingham hallmarks for 1905, 19.2cm. high.   £990

A Sterling silver vase with Celtic style motif, Towle Co., Newburyport, Massachusetts, circa 1900, approximately 30 troy oz., 9¾in. high.   £314

A pair of late 19th century Turkish vases, one for burning incence, the other for rose-water, 25cm. high - 50.5ozs.   £1,900

An Edwardian Irish spot-hammered flaring vase applied with foliate decorated scroll handles, Goldsmiths & Silversmiths Co. Ltd., Dublin 1903, 8¼in., 28.75 oz.   £572

VESTA CASES

A Victorian fisherman's creel vesta case, the interior with Essex crystal depicting two trout, by Thos. Johnson, 1882, 5.5cm. long.   £1,750

An Edwardian circular vesta case, the front chased with a Victorian Rifle Volunteers shooting competition, Birmingham, 1906.   £196

A Victorian combined vesta case and cachou box, engraved all over with leafage, 'Cachous', Birmingham, 1887.   £130

VINAIGRETTES

An attractive late Victorian vinaigrette, the cover set with turquoise and incised with a name in Persian script, by William Summers, 1888.   £90

A cylindrical double-ended pill box/vinaigrette, 3oz., London, 1917.   £50

A Victorian novelty vinaigrette by Sampson Mordan & Co. modelled as a walnut, the grille pierced and engraved with a flower within a circle, circa 1880.   £280

WINE COOLERS

An Elkington plate wine cooler and stand, stamped Cunard White Star, 18¼in. high.   £418

One of a pair of wine coolers, stamped Georg Jensen GI 925S 289, 9.8cm. high, 29oz. 9dwt.   £3,780

A Victorian silver plated ice bucket, by Elkington & Co., circa 1880, 8½in. high, together with three other ice buckets.   £644

TEDDY BEARS

A golden plush covered teddy bear with hump and Steiff button in ear, 14in. high. £352

A honey plush covered teddy bear with boot button eyes, 14in. high, Steiff button in ear, circa 1903. £820

An early 20th century blonde plush, straw filled teddy bear with black and orange glass eyes, 50cm. high. £220

A blonde plush covered teddy bear, with boot button eyes, long arms and felt pads, 10½in. high, circa 1910. £308

Alfonzo — a very rare short red plush teddy bear, with button eyes, excelsior stuffing and felt pads, dressed as a Russian, 13in. high, with Steiff button. £12,100

A golden plush covered teddy bear with boot button eyes, wide apart ears, and Steiff button in ear, 16in. high. £1,210

A cinammon plush covered bear with large black boot button eyes, 29in. long, Steiff button in ear, circa 1904. £1,870

A blonde plush covered teddy bear with boot button eyes, 17in. high with Steiff button in ear. £440

A light brown plush covered teddy bear with boot button eyes, 21in. high, by Steiff, circa 1905. £300

TOYS

'Autobus', a printed and painted tinplate open 'Berlin' type double deck omnibus, by Lehmann, circa 1912, 8in. long. £770

A rare printed and painted tinplate high-wing, cabin monoplane, with two blade propeller and helicopter blades, 8½in. long, German, circa 1920. £176

'The Performing Sea-Lion', a painted tinplate sea-lion with clockwork mechanism, by Lehmann, circa 1910, 7½in. long. £209

A Meccano No. 1 Aeroplane Constructor Outfit, with instructions, in original box, circa 1937. £220

A painted wooden toy stable with stalls and alcoves above, with fretted decorations, 18in. high, French. £154

A painted wooden dolls' house of four bays and three storeys, 50in. high x 46in. wide on stand, circa 1840. £4,950

Dinky Supertoys Foden 'Mobilgas' tanker, fair condition. £55

Nomura Toys, battery operated tinplate Robbie the Robot, 32.5cm., 1956. £850

A printed and painted tinplate motorcycle and sidecar, lithographed gentleman rider and lady passenger, 4½in. long, German, 1920's. £418

TOYS

Dinky Supertoys 514 Guy Van, advertising 'Slumberland', in original paintwork, with box. £176

'Mac 700', a printed and painted tinplate motorbike and rider, with clockwork mechanism, by Arnold, W. Germany, circa 1955 (one arm damaged, slightly worn), 7½in. long. £132

Dinky Supertoys, 919 Guy van, advertising 'Golden Shred', in original paintwork, unboxed, slightly chipped. £77

A rubber inflatable Mickey Mouse 41cm. high. £28

Dinky rare pre-war French Set No. 60 Avions, including Arc-en-ciel, Potez Type 58, Hanriot Type 180T, Dewoitine Type 500, Breguet Type Corsaire and Autogire, in original box, circa 1937. £5,500

A very fine French tinplate dolls' pram, the body with blue and gold lithograph paintwork, 23cm. £1,600

Scamold clockwork die-cast Grand Prix racing cars, including ERA, Maserati and Alta, in original boxes. £418

Lineol made 5/32, Wehrmacht standard bearer, tin colour one shoulder, 1938. £60

Britains set 1321, large armoured car with swivelling gun, khaki finish with white rubber treaded tyres in original box (E-G, box G)1937. £280

A 1930's Lines Bros. pedal car with wooden body and chassis, mock honeycomb radiator grill, and pneumatic tyres 47in. long. £775

A rare and early hand enamelled tinplate woman pushing a cart, with caged goose, probably by Gunthermann, circa 1903, 7½in. long. £462

A Marx clockwork Rookie Pilot, boxed. £90

A painted wooden dolls' house of two separated storeys, with original wall and some floor coverings. £308

A good metal miniature toy zoetrope on ornate metal base with a quantity of picture strips, marked 'Made in Germany'. £209

A Meccano No. 2 Electrical Experiments Set, in original box, 1930's. £198

'Caravan Novelty', a lithographed tinplate gypsy caravan, by Chad Valley for Jacobs, circa 1937, 6¼in. long. £165

A painted wooden dolls' house, simulating stone with red roof and bay windows flanking the marbelised porch, 43in. high. £715

A Dinky 917 Guy van, advertising 'Spratt's', in original paintwork, fair condition, unboxed. £132

TOYS

A Carette lithographed tinplate clockwork model of a four seater tonneau, with rubber tyred spoked wheels, handbrake, and side lamps, 33cm. long.
£1,900

A rare humorous composition toy, modelled as a red faced man with startled eyes hanging on to a runaway donkey, 6½in. long, mid 19th century, German. £710

A short plush covered nodding Boston terrier, with pull growl and lower jaw movement, 22in. long, circa 1910, French.
£330

A fine late 19th century dolls' house, the front removable to reveal a six roomed interior with original papers, 41½in. wide. £750

An early Japanese lithographed tinplate travelling boy, with clockwork mechanism, 1930's, 8in. high. £440

A mahogany dolls' house of two bays and two storeys with castellated bow window, 47in. high, late 19th century.
£1,430

An early hand painted maid, standing at an ironing board, holding an iron and a winged collar, 8in. high, probably by Gunthermann, circa 1903.
£550

French Dinky Supertoys, Set No. 60, Coffret Cadeau Avions, in original box. £275

A late nineteenth century painted wood and composition rocking horse, with jockey rider, 10½in. long, German.
£715

TRAVEL POSTERS

'Cleethorpes', published by
L.N.E.R., designed by
Templeton, 102 x 64cm.
£70

'Queen of Scots, All Pullman',
designed by Fred Taylor.
£750

'Sunny Worthing, All The Year
Round', designed by V. E.
Danvers, 1947.   £150

'Cleethorpes', designed by
Foster Jarrett.   £270

'Take Me by The Flying
Scotsman', designed by A. R.
Thomson.   £1,300

'Tynemouth', designed by
Alfred Lambart.   £520

'I'm Ready, Take Your Dog
With You By Rail',   £240

'Cunard Line , Monarchs of
the Sea, Liverpool, New York,
Boston', 102 x 64cm.   £500

'Torquay, Devon's Riviera',
published by G.W.R.,
102 x 64cm.   £320

'The Continent Via Harwich', designed by Higgins, published by L.N.E.R. £260

'George Stephenson Started Us 100 Years Ago', published by L.N.E.R. £100

'Eastbourne', published by Southern Railway, designed by Kenneth D. Shoesmith, 1929. £400

'The Silver Jubilee, Britain's First Streamline Train', published by L.N.E.R. £340

'Cruden Bay', designed by H. G. Gawthorn, published by L.N.E.R. £1,300

'Harrogate', designed by H.G. Gawthorn. £240

'Harwich—Zeebrugge, Through Trucks To and From the Continent', designed by Austin Cooper. £100

'Scarborough, It's Quicker By Rail', designed by Frank H. Mason. £200

'Ripon', published by L.N.E.R. designed by Walter Spradbury. £65

WEATHERVANES

Copper car weathervane, Prides Crossing, Mass., circa 1914, 3ft.8in. long.   £3,906

A copper and zinc horse and sulky weather-vane, attributed to W. A. Snow, Boston, Massachusetts, late 19th century, 37in. wide.
£4,545

A fine and rare moulded and gilt copper weathervane, American, 19th century, model-led in the form of a centaur with bow and arrow, retaining traces of original gilding, 32in. high, 40in. long.   £42,235

A cast iron horse weathervane, American, 19th century, of a full bodied figure of a horse with raised foreleg, 35in. wide.
£4,873

'Mayflower' silhouette weathervane, attributed to E. G. Washburne & Co., N.Y., circa 1920, 36in. long.   £1,328

Cast zinc and copper weathervane, by J. Howard & Company, West Bridgewater, Massachusetts, circa 1875, 24¾in. wide.
£1,714

'Foxhound' weathervane, L. W. Cushing & Sons, Waltham, Mass., circa 1883, with traces of gold leaf and weathered verdigris surface, 27in. long.
£8,741

A hollow gilt copper and cast iron weather-vane in the form of a bull, American, 1885-1890, bull 39in. long, 23in. high.   £2,309

WOOD

An Indian ebony watch and ink stand, decorated with five elephants and with a quill rest, 8in. high. £110

An inlaid wood trying plane, America, 19th century, the stock and wedge of plane inlaid with contrasting woods and bone in variety of Masonic symbols, 23in. long. £511

A crow decoy, attributed to Gus Wilson, Maine, first half 20th century, with carved wings and tail, 9½in. high. £312

Early 20th century standing male figure, 28in. high. £168

Camel carousel figure, possibly New York State, 19th century, the stylised carved and painted figure of a camel with hemp tail and fringed leather and canvas saddle, 48in. wide. £5,714

A carved and painted wood male figure by Henry Boehm, Allentown, Pennsylvania, circa 1920, modelled in the form of a man with a pipe, 12½in. high. £292

A decorative carved and painted preening yellowleg, A. Elmer Crowell, East Harwich, Massachusetts, 1862-1952, 14in. high. £5,594

Carved and painted counter figure, probably New York City, late 19th century, the stylised head of a bearded Turk wearing a turban, 19½in. high. £1,428

Late 19th/early 20th century carved and painted wooden hanging clock shelf, possibly Virginia, 21½in. high, 14¾in. wide. £279

WOOD

One of a pair of German carved walnut hunting trophies, circa 1880, depicting captured game, 31in. high. £443

A painted wooden caricature figure of Charlie Chaplin, by Betterway, Vienna, 52cm. high, circa 1930. £170

An eider decoy, Monhegan Island, Maine, late 19th century, hollow carved with inletted head, (age cracks, paint and wood loss), 11in. high, 21in. long. £10,795

Late 19th century 'Factory Girl' large painted sled, America, 3ft.8½in. long, 19in. wide. £1,904

Small carousel stander, mounted as a rocking horse, circa 1900, 27in. high, 29in. long. £892

A carved and painted blue jay, carved by A. Elmer Crowell, East Harwich, Massachusetts, early 20th century, life-size figure, 23.1cm. high. £625

A carved and painted pine counter top figure of a fireman, signed by Lewis E. Tallier, Roxbury, Massachusetts, circa 1915, 27½in. high. £7,797

A lacquered rosewood and gilt panel by N. Brunet, deeply carved in intaglio with two pumas by a lakeside, mounted on giltwood frame, 50.7cm. x 99.5cm. £2,750

Late 19th century carved and painted black figure of a male acrobat, possibly Italy, 31in. high. £1,726

Index

251

INDEX

INDEX

INDEX

INDEX